SCIENTIFIC PROGRESS GOES "BOINK"

Other Books by Bill Watterson

Calvin and Hobbes
Something Under the Bed Is Drooling
Yukon Ho!
Weirdos From Another Planet!
The Revenge of the Baby-Sat

Treasury Collections

The Essential Calvin and Hobbes
The Calvin and Hobbes Lazy Sunday Book
The Authoritative Calvin and Hobbes

SCIENTIFIC PROGRESS GOES "BOINK"

A Calvin and Hobbes Collection by Bill Watterson

SCHOLASTIC INC.
New York Toronto London Auckland Sydney

Calvin and Hobbes is distributed internationally
by Universal Press Syndicate.

ISBN 0-590-45678-4

24 23 22 21 20 19 18 17 16 15 14 13   9/9 0 1 2/0

Printed in the U.S.A.   02

First Scholastic Printing, January 1992

Printed on recycled paper.

CalViN and HObbEs
by WATTERSON

PHWPPT!

THPWIPBTH

AHHH..

DEAR, SOMETIME I WANT YOU TO LOOK AT THAT DISCOLORED SPOT ON THE RUG. IT SEEMS TO BE GETTING BIGGER ALL THE TIME.

MAY I LEAVE THE TABLE? LIKE RIGHT NOW?

I want that truck, Twinky.

IT'S MINE, MOE. I BROUGHT IT FROM HOME.

I said gimme the truck.

MOE, YOU CAN'T JUST *TAKE* THINGS FROM PEOPLE BECAUSE YOU'RE BIGGER!

I'm not taking it. You're **giving** it to me because we'll both be so much happier that way.

HOW TOUCHING.

MOE, GIVE ME MY TRUCK BACK. IT'S NOT YOURS.

It is **now**. You gave it to me.

I DIDN'T HAVE MUCH CHOICE, *DID* I ?! IT WAS EITHER GIVE UP THE TRUCK OR GET PUNCHED!

So?

SO I ONLY "GAVE" IT TO YOU BECAUSE YOU'RE BIGGER AND MEANER THAN ME!

Yeah? ...So?

THE FORENSIC MARVEL HAS REDUCED MY LOGIC TO SHAMBLES.

You're saying you changed your mind about getting punched?

THAT NO-GOOD, ROTTEN MOE! HE WON'T GIVE MY TRUCK BACK TO ME. THE OAF WILL PROBABLY BREAK IT, TOO.

SHOULD I STEAL IT BACK? I KNOW STEALING IS WRONG, BUT *HE* STOLE IT FROM *ME*, AND IF I DON'T STEAL IT BACK, MOE WILL JUST KEEP IT, AND THAT'S NOT FAIR.

THEY SAY TWO WRONGS DON'T MAKE A RIGHT, BUT WHAT ARE YOU SUPPOSED TO *DO* THEN? JUST LET THE BIGGEST GUY MAKE HIS OWN RULES ALL THE TIME? LET MIGHT MAKE RIGHT?

... THAT SOUNDS REASONABLE.

BY GOLLY, I **AM** GOING TO STEAL MY TRUCK BACK FROM MOE! IT'S MINE AND HE HAS NO RIGHT TO HAVE IT!

I'LL JUST SNEAK UP BEHIND THE SWINGS HERE, AND WHEN MOE'S NOT LOOKING, I'LL RUN UP, GRAB THE TRUCK AND TAKE OFF!

THIS PLAYGROUND SHOULD HAVE ONE OF THOSE AUTOMATIC INSURANCE MACHINES LIKE THEY HAVE IN AIRPORTS.

OK, MOE'S GOT HIS BACK TO ME! NOW I'LL ZIP OVER, STEAL MY TRUCK BACK AND RUN LIKE CRAZY!

HE'LL NEVER KNOW WHAT HIT HIM! BY THE TIME HE SEES THE TRUCK IS GONE, I'LL BE A MILE AWAY! IT'S A FAIL-PROOF PLAN! NOTHING CAN GO WRONG! IT'S A SNAP!

THERE'S NO REASON TO HESITATE. IT'LL BE OVER IN A SPLIT SECOND, AND I'LL SURE BE GLAD TO HAVE MY TRUCK BACK! I'LL JUST DO IT AND BE DONE! NOTHING TO IT! IT'S EASY!

OBVIOUSLY MY BODY DOESN'T BELIEVE A WORD MY BRAIN IS SAYING.

PHOOEY, WHO AM I KIDDING? I'D NEVER GET AWAY WITH STEALING MY TRUCK BACK FROM MOE. THE UGLY GALOOT IS THE SIZE OF A BUICK.

HMM... SINCE I CAN'T **FIGHT** HIM, MAYBE I SHOULD TRY **TALKING** TO HIM. MAYBE IF I REASONED WITH HIM, HE'D SEE **MY** SIDE.

MAYBE HE'D REALIZE THAT STEALING HURTS PEOPLE, AND MAYBE HE'D RETURN MY TRUCK **WILLINGLY.**

MAYBE IF I'M REALLY LUCKY I WON'T GO THROUGH LIFE WITH THE NICKNAME "OMELET FACE."

LISTEN, MOE, THAT'S *MY* TRUCK, AND I WANT IT BACK!

Yeah?

YEAH! IT'S MY FAVORITE TRUCK. YOU HAD NO RIGHT TO TAKE IT!

Yeah?

YEAH! SO GIVE IT BACK! *NOW!*

I'll fight you for it.

I'LL BET MY AUTOPSY REVEALS MY MOUTH IS TOO BIG.

C'mon, wimp!

I'M NOT GOING TO FIGHT YOU, MOE! IF YOU WON'T GIVE ME MY TRUCK BACK, *FINE!* GO AHEAD AND KEEP IT!

YOU'RE THE ONE WHO HAS TO LIVE WITH YOURSELF! *I* CAN'T MAKE YOU DO WHAT'S RIGHT! YOU CAN *HAVE* THE STUPID TRUCK!

OK, thanks! Heh heh.

HEY, KID, IF YOU'RE NOT GONNA SWING, GET OFF AND LET SOMEONE *ELSE* ON, HUH?

...SO MOE STOLE MY TRUCK, AND WHEN I TRIED TO GET IT BACK, MOE WANTED TO FIGHT ME FOR IT. I DIDN'T WANT TO FIGHT, SO I WALKED AWAY AND MOE KEPT MY TRUCK.

I DON'T UNDERSTAND IT, HOBBES. WHAT MAKES SOME PEOPLE SO GREEDY AND MEAN?

WHY IS IT THAT SOME PEOPLE DON'T CARE WHAT'S WRONG AND RIGHT? WHY DON'T PEOPLE TRY TO BE NICE TO EACH OTHER?

THE PROBLEM WITH PEOPLE IS THAT THEY'RE ONLY HUMAN.

WELL, *YOU'RE* LUCKY YOU DON'T HAVE TO *BE* ONE.

8

Calvin and Hobbes

by WATTERSON

TIGERS ARE GREAT! THEY'RE THE TOAST OF THE TOWN. LIFE'S ALWAYS BETTER WHEN A TIGER'S AROUND!

CONSIDERING I OUTRANK YOU, I DON'T THINK I SHOULD HAVE TO DO THAT!

THIS MEETING OF THE TOP-SECRET CLUB G.R.O.S.S. (GET RID OF SLIMY GIRLS) WILL COME TO ORDER, SUPREME DICTATOR-FOR-LIFE CALVIN PRESIDING. ALL SALUTE!

OK, THE FIRST ORDER OF BUSINESS: PRESIDENT-AND-FIRST-TIGER HOBBES WILL READ THE MINUTES OF OUR LAST MEETING.

THANK YOU. 10:30 A.M.: READ MINUTES OF PREVIOUS MEETING. 10:31: DEBATED SO-CALLED "EDITORIAL SLANT" OF MINUTES. MUCH NONSENSE AND COMMOTION FROM DICTATOR-FOR-LIFE.

"NONSENSE"?!

10:32: PRESIDENT-AND-FIRST-TIGER OFFERS REASONABLE SOLUTION, BUT DICTATOR-FOR-LIFE TAKES NEEDLESS EXCEPTION.

REASONABLE SOLUTION?!? YOU TOLD ME TO GO JUMP IN A LAKE!

10:33: BLOWS EXCHANGED, DICTATOR-FOR-LIFE RECEIVES COMEUPPANCE.

HA! I BEAT YOU FAIR AND SQUARE! THESE MINUTES ARE NOTHING BUT LIES!

CALL ME A LIAR, WILL YOU?

BY GOLLY, I'LL CALL YOU WORSE THAN THAT!

CHOWDERHEAD!

MORON!

OGRE!

FLEABAG!

(PANT, PANT) TRUCE?

(GASP, PANT) OK, TRUCE.

WELL, ANOTHER PRODUCTIVE MEETING! WHAT A GREAT CLUB!

10

CALVIN, I'M TELLING YOUR PARENTS ABOUT THIS! NOW LET ME IN!

PIPE DOWN, WILL YA ROZ? HOBBES AND I CAN HARDLY HEAR THE TV!

YOU'RE NOT SUPPOSED TO *BE* WATCHING TELEVISION!

HEY, IF YOU GO RENT US A VCR AND A MOVIE, WE'LL PUT THE TV NEAR A WINDOW SO YOU CAN WATCH TOO!

LET ME IN!

ARE YOU 18? YOU COULD GET US "VENUSIAN VAMPIRE VIXENS"!

CAL-VIN!

HANG ON, ROZ. THE PHONE IS RINGING!

I HOPE IT'S YOUR PARENTS! I HOPE THEY ASK TO TALK TO ME! BOY, YOU'LL BE IN TROUBLE *THEN*!

IT'S YOUR BOYFRIEND, CHARLIE! SHOULD I TELL HIM YOU'RE INDISPOSED? HA HA!

NO! LET ME TALK TO HIM!

SAY CHAS, DON'T YOU THINK YOU'RE SETTLING FOR TOO LITTLE IN THE GIRLFRIEND DEPARTMENT?

ISN'T IT GREAT TO GET OUT OF THE HOUSE ALONE TOGETHER FOR A CHANGE?

IT'S SO NICE AND QUIET. WE SHOULD DO THIS MORE OFTEN.

CALVIN, YOU'VE GOT FIVE SECONDS TO OPEN THE DOOR BEFORE I BREAK A WINDOW!

I'M TELLING YOU CHUCK, YOUR GIRLFRIEND IS A PSYCHO! I HOPE YOU'RE NOT MAKING ANY LONG-RANGE PLANS AROUND HER.

CALVIN and HOBBES

by WATTERSON

GISZH!... GISZH!...

..GISZH!

OH, NO! IT'S THE MIDDLE OF RECESS AND THERE'S A TYRANNOSAURUS ON THE PLAYGROUND!

THE KIDS AT THE TOP OF THE SLIDE ARE THE FIRST TO GO! HOW IRONIC THAT THEY HAD PUSHED AND FOUGHT EACH OTHER TO BE THERE!

PANDEMONIUM ENSUES! TEACHERS LINE THE KIDS UP TO GO INSIDE, BUT THAT PROVES TO BE A SAD MISTAKE!

WALKING QUIETLY IN SINGLE FILE, THE KIDS ARE GOBBLED UP LIKE CHILDREN McNUGGETS!

SOON THE PLAYGROUND IS EMPTY! IT'S ALL HIS! THE TYRANNOSAUR LETS OUT A TRIUMPHANT ROAR!

SAY, WHERE'S CALVIN? RECESS IS OVER. DIDN'T HE SEE US LINE UP TO COME IN?

I SEE HIM, MISS WORMWOOD! HE'S OUT BY THE SWINGS AND HE'S YELLING OR SOMETHING!

Calvin and Hobbes
by WATTERSON

REALLY? WHAT DID YOU DO?

THAT BIG, DUMB BULLY MOE PUNCHED ME AT SCHOOL YESTERDAY.

WELL, FIRST I SKIDDED ACROSS THE PLAYGROUND. THEN I CAROMED OFF A ROCK AND...

I WISH I HAD MORE FRIENDS, BUT PEOPLE ARE SUCH JERKS.

IF YOU CAN JUST GET MOST PEOPLE TO IGNORE YOU AND LEAVE YOU ALONE, YOU'RE DOING GOOD.

IF YOU CAN FIND EVEN ONE PERSON YOU REALLY LIKE, YOU'RE LUCKY.

...AND IF THAT PERSON CAN ALSO STAND *YOU*, YOU'RE *REALLY* LUCKY.

WHAT IF YOU FIND SOMEONE YOU CAN TALK TO WHILE YOU EAT APPLES ON A BRIGHT FALL MORNING?

WELL, YEAH... I SUPPOSE THERE'S NO POINT IN GETTING GREEDY, IS THERE?

16

MAN, THIS IS BORING!

HOW AM I EVER GOING TO READ THREE WHOLE PAGES OF THIS BY TOMORROW? IT'S IMPOSSIBLE!

...IMPOSSIBLE?? WHY, *NOTHING'S* IMPOSSIBLE!

NOT FOR... **STUPENDOUS MAN!** BUM BA BA **DAA** DUM ♪ BUM BA BA **DAA** DUM..

YES! IT'S... *STUPENDOUS MAN!* FRIEND OF FREEDOM! OPPONENT OF OPPRESSION! LOVER OF LIBERTY!

GREAT MOONS OF JUPITER! CALVIN (*STUPENDOUS MAN'S* 6-YEAR-OLD ALTER EGO) HAS THREE PAGES OF BORING HOMEWORK TO READ! IT'S *TYRANNY!*

ALTHOUGH *STUPENDOUS MAN* COULD EASILY READ THE ASSIGNMENT WITH STUPENDOUS *HIGH-SPEED VISION,* THE MASKED MAN OF MIGHT HAS A BOLDER PLAN!

WITH STUPENDOUS POWERS OF REASONING, THE CAPED COMBATANT CONCLUDES THERE'S NO NEED FOR HOMEWORK IF *THERE'S NO SCHOOL TOMORROW!*

A BLINDING BOLT OF BLAZING CRIMSON CAREENS ACROSS THE SKY! IT'S *STUPENDOUS MAN!*

SECONDS LATER, THE AMAZING MARVEL ALIGHTS UPON AN OBSERVATORY TELESCOPE AT MOUNT PALOMAR!

WITH STUPENDOUS STRENGTH, *STUPENDOUS MAN* CAREFULLY UNSCREWS THE GIANT LENS...

...AND BLASTS INTO SPACE WITH IT!

STUPENDOUS MAN CIRCLES THE EARTH WITH A 200-INCH TELESCOPE LENS!

ALIGNED PERFECTLY WITH THE SUN, THE MAGNIFYING LENS FOCUSES THE TERRIBLE SOLAR ENERGY...

...AND FRIES A CERTAIN ELEMENTARY SCHOOL 'CLEAN OFF THE MAP!'

NOW MILD-MANNERED CALVIN HAS NO NEED TO DO HIS HOMEWORK EVER AGAIN! LIBERTY PREVAILS!

HOW'S YOUR HOMEWORK COMING, CALVIN?

UH OH, IT'S MY ARCH-NEMESIS, **MOM-LADY!** SHE CAN'T DISCOVER MY SECRET IDENTITY!

CALVIN? ARE YOU DOING YOUR HOMEWORK IN THERE?

QUICKLY, **STUPENDOUS MAN** LEAPS INTO THE CLOSET TO CHANGE BACK INTO HIS 6-YEAR-OLD ALTER EGO, MILD-MANNERED CALVIN!

CALVIN? ARE YOU IN HERE?

UNFORTUNATELY, **STUPENDOUS MAN'S** CAPE IS CAUGHT IN MILD-MANNERED CALVIN'S ZIPPER! CURSES!

THIS IS GOING TO BE A GOOD ONE, I CAN TELL.

GEEZ, MOM! CAN'T A GUY HAVE A LITTLE PRIVACY?!

AND WHY, MAY I ASK, ARE YOU STANDING IN YOUR UNDERWEAR IN THE CLOSET?

OH, NO REASON. UM... I WAS HOT.

YOU'RE **SUPPOSED** TO BE DOING YOUR HOMEWORK!

I DON'T NEED TO DO IT NOW, THANKS TO **STUPENDOUS MAN!**

OH YEAH?

IT WAS GREAT! HE FRIED THE SCHOOL WITH A BIG MAGNIFYING LENS IN SPACE! I'M SURE IT WILL BE IN ALL THE PAPERS TOMORROW.

BOY, SHE'LL BE IN TROUBLE WHEN SHE GIVES ME MY COSTUME BACK. **BIG** TROUBLE.

CALVIN and HOBBES by WATTERSON

I'M HO-OME!

HI, CALVIN. WHATCHA DOIN'?

OOF, GET THIS BIG LUMMOX OFF ME.

LOOK AT YOU! YOU DIDN'T EVEN CHANGE OUT OF YOUR SCHOOL CLOTHES!

HOW COULD I?! I DIDN'T EVEN GET IN THE DOOR!

EVERY DAY THIS MANIAC IS SO GLAD TO SEE ME THAT HE BLASTS OUT LIKE A BIG ORANGE TORPEDO! A *DOG* WILL JUST WAG ITS TAIL, BUT OF COURSE A *TIGER* HAS TO *POUNCE* ON YOU! STUPID ANIMAL!

HE POUNCES ON YOU?

OH, AND DON'T THINK HE DOESN'T ENJOY THE CUNNING AND TREACHERY OF IT ALL! TIGERS *LIVE* FOR THE THRILL OF A SNEAK ATTACK! IT'S THEIR EVIL NATURE!

HE'S JUST SITTING THERE.

OH, SURE, *BIG* DISGUISE! LIKE NO ONE CAN FATHOM THE SAVAGE MIND OF A JUNGLE CAT! HA! HE'S A KILLER TO THE CORE!

I WISH MY PARENTS WOULD MOVE. MY DIARY IS GETTING WEIRDER EVERY DAY.

YEAH, *YOU* KNOW WHO I'M TALKING ABOUT! WIPE OFF THAT GRIN OR *I'LL* DO IT *FOR* YOU!

I'VE GOT AN IDEA, DAD.

MAYBE I'D GET BETTER GRADES IF YOU OFFERED ME $1 FOR EVERY "D", $5 FOR EVERY "C", $10 FOR EVERY "B", AND $50 FOR EVERY "A"!

I'M NOT GOING TO *BRIBE* YOU, CALVIN. YOU SHOULD APPLY YOURSELF FOR YOUR OWN GOOD.

RATS. I THOUGHT I COULD MAKE AN EASY FOUR BUCKS.

HELLO? VALLEY HARDWARE? YES, I'M CALLING TO SEE IF YOU SELL BLASTING CAPS, DETONATORS, TIMERS AND WIRE.

JUST THE WIRE? OK, FORGET IT. DO YOU RENT BULLDOZERS OR BACKHOES?

NO, NO, A ROTOTILLER WON'T DO AT ALL. I NEED SOMETHING MORE LIKE A WRECKING BALL. DO YOU KNOW WHERE I COULD GET ANYTHING LIKE THAT? NO? OK, GOODBYE.

LOOKS LIKE ANOTHER BORING DAY, HOBBES.

I CAN'T SLEEP, HOBBES. I'VE BEEN THINKING.

WHAT ABOUT?

WELL, SUPPOSE THERE'S NO AFTERLIFE. THAT WOULD MEAN *THIS* LIFE IS ALL YOU GET.

AND *THAT* WOULD MEAN I'M SITTING HERE IN BED AS PRECIOUS MOMENTS OF MY ALL-TOO-SHORT LIFE DISAPPEAR FOREVER.

HONEY, WAKE UP. DO YOU HEAR THE TELEVISION ON?

by WATTERSON

GOSH, IT'S 1:30 AND I'M STILL AWAKE.

SOMEONE MUST'VE WAYLAID MR. SANDMAN.

I JUST CAN'T... GET... COMFORTABLE.

MMF.

I'M EXHAUSTED, BUT I CAN'T FALL ASLEEP.

MAYBE IF I JUST LIE STILL AND THINK ABOUT HOW GOOD IT FEELS TO BE IN BED, AND HOW SOFT THE PILLOW IS, AND HOW VERY, VERY TIRED I AM...

...PHOOEY, THIS ISN'T WORKING. ALL I WANT IS TO GET SOME SLEEP. THIS IS AWFUL.

CALVIN?

GEE MOM, ARE YOU AWAKE TOO?

IT'S TIME TO GET UP.

IT *CAN'T* BE! IT'S THE MIDDLE OF THE NIGHT AND I HAVEN'T SLEPT A WINK YET!

CALVIN?

C'MON, UP AND AT 'EM.

HUZBGH

blink blink

THIS IS GOING TO BE A BAD DAY.

THE STRANGEST THING HAPPENED TO ME A FEW MINUTES AGO.

OH? WHAT?

I WAS MINDING MY OWN BUSINESS, WHEN SUDDENLY I WAS ZAPPED INTO SOME SORT OF SPACE VOID VORTEX!

THERE I WATCHED HELPLESSLY AS AN EVIL DUPLICATE OF MYSELF FROM A PARALLEL UNIVERSE TOOK MY PLACE ON EARTH, AND...

WHAT HAVE YOU DONE *NOW*?

NO, NO, SEE, IT WASN'T *ME*...

HEH HEH HEH!

AHA! I SEE YOU! SNEAKING UP TO POUNCE ON ME, EH?

PHOOEY.

YOU SEE WHY *MOST* TIGERS DON'T CHUCKLE TO THEMSELVES.

WANT TO PLAY A GREAT GAME I INVENTED?

OK.

IT'S CALLED "GROSS OUT." YOU SAY THE GROSSEST THING YOU CAN IMAGINE, AND THEN I TRY TO THINK OF SOMETHING EVEN GROSSER.

WHOEVER COMES UP WITH THE GROSSEST THING GETS A POINT, AND WE PLAY UNTIL SOMEONE GETS 50 POINTS, OK?

I THINK I ALREADY KNOW WHO'S GOING TO WIN.

IT'S WEIRD. NOBODY HAS EVER PLAYED A WHOLE GAME WITH ME.

Calvin and Hobbes

by WATTERSON

WOW, HONEY, YOU'RE MISSING A BEAUTIFUL SUNSET OUT HERE!

I'LL COUNT TO 10, AND THEN... *POW!*

DAD, HOW COME OLD PHOTOGRAPHS ARE ALWAYS BLACK AND WHITE? DIDN'T THEY HAVE COLOR FILM BACK THEN?

SURE THEY DID. IN FACT, THOSE OLD PHOTOGRAPHS *ARE* IN COLOR. IT'S JUST THE *WORLD* WAS BLACK AND WHITE THEN.

REALLY?

YEP. THE WORLD DIDN'T TURN COLOR UNTIL SOMETIME IN THE 1930s, AND IT WAS PRETTY GRAINY COLOR FOR A WHILE, TOO.

THAT'S REALLY WEIRD.

WELL, TRUTH IS STRANGER THAN FICTION.

BUT THEN WHY ARE OLD *PAINTINGS* IN COLOR?' IF THE WORLD WAS BLACK AND WHITE, WOULDN'T ARTISTS HAVE PAINTED IT THAT WAY?

NOT NECESSARILY. A LOT OF GREAT ARTISTS WERE INSANE.

BUT...BUT HOW COULD THEY HAVE PAINTED IN COLOR ANYWAY? WOULDN'T THEIR PAINTS HAVE BEEN SHADES OF GRAY BACK THEN?

OF COURSE, BUT THEY TURNED COLORS LIKE EVERYTHING ELSE DID IN THE '30s.

SO WHY DIDN'T OLD BLACK AND WHITE PHOTOS TURN COLOR TOO?

BECAUSE THEY WERE COLOR PICTURES OF BLACK AND WHITE, REMEMBER?

THE WORLD IS A COMPLICATED PLACE, HOBBES.

WHENEVER IT SEEMS THAT WAY, I TAKE A NAP IN A TREE AND WAIT FOR DINNER.

PAY ATTENTION TO ME.

I'VE GOT TO WRITE A REPORT FOR SCHOOL.

WHAT'S YOUR TOPIC?

BATS. CAN YOU IMAGINE ANYTHING MORE STUPID?

HECK, *I* DON'T KNOW ANYTHING ABOUT BATS! HOW AM I SUPPOSED TO WRITE A REPORT ON A SUBJECT I KNOW NOTHING ABOUT?! IT'S IMPOSSIBLE!

I SUPPOSE RESEARCH IS OUT OF THE QUESTION.

OH, LIKE I'M GOING TO LEARN ABOUT BATS AND *THEN* WRITE A REPORT?! GIVE ME A BREAK!

HELLO, SUSIE? THIS IS CALVIN. YOU KNOW THIS REPORT WE'RE SUPPOSED TO WRITE FOR SCHOOL? YEAH. MY TOPIC IS BATS. WHAT'S YOURS?

ELEPHANTS? HMM. WELL, ARE YOU GOING TO THE LIBRARY TO LOOK UP ELEPHANTS? YOU ARE? GREAT!

WHILE YOU'RE THERE, COULD YOU RESEARCH BATS TOO, AND MAKE COPIES OF ALL THE INFORMATION YOU FIND, AND MAYBE UNDERLINE THE IMPORTANT PARTS FOR ME, AND SORT OF OUTLINE IT, SO I WOULDN'T HAVE TO READ IT ALL?

HOW'D IT GO?

I REALLY LOATHE GIRLS.

ALL RIGHT, CLASS, WHO WOULD LIKE TO GIVE HIS REPORT FIRST?

I WOULD! I WOULD!

WHY CALVIN, WHAT A SURPRISE TO SEE *YOU* VOLUNTEER! YOU MUST HAVE DONE A GOOD JOB. GO TO THE FRONT OF THE CLASS.

OH BOY!

NOW LET'S ALL PAY ATTENTION. GO AHEAD, CALVIN.

THANK YOU. BEFORE I BEGIN, I'D LIKE EVERYONE TO NOTICE THAT MY REPORT IS IN A PROFESSIONAL, CLEAR PLASTIC BINDER.

THAT'S VERY NICE. GO AHEAD.

WHEN A REPORT LOOKS THIS GOOD, YOU KNOW IT'LL GET AN "A". THAT'S A TIP, KIDS. WRITE IT DOWN.

MY REPORT IS ON BATS. ...AHEM...

"DUSK! WITH A CREEPY, TINGLING SENSATION, YOU HEAR THE FLUTTERING OF LEATHERY WINGS! *BATS!* WITH GLOWING RED EYES AND GLISTENING FANGS, THESE UNSPEAKABLE GIANT BUGS DROP ONTO..."

BATS AREN'T BUGS!!

LOOK, WHO'S GIVING THE REPORT? *YOU* CHONDERHEADS ...OR *ME*?!

CALVIN, I'D LIKE TO SEE YOU A MOMENT.

MAN ALIVE! CAN YOU BELIEVE WHAT MY TEACHER WROTE ON MY REPORT?

SHE SAYS I OBVIOUSLY DID NO RESEARCH WHATSOEVER ON BATS AND THAT MY SCIENTIFIC ILLUSTRATION LOOKS LIKE I TRACED THE BATMAN LOGO AND ADDED FANGS!

SHE'S PRETTY PERCEPTIVE.

SHE DIDN'T EVEN GIVE ME CREDIT FOR MY PROFESSIONAL CLEAR PLASTIC BINDER!

WHAT DID YOUR PARENTS HAVE TO SAY?

NOTHING. AND IF YOU'LL GIVE ME A HAND HERE, IT WILL STAY THAT WAY.

Calvin and Hobbes
by WATTERSON

I'VE BEEN THINKING, HOBBES.

ON A WEEKEND?

WELL, IT WASN'T ON PURPOSE...

I BELIEVE HISTORY IS A FORCE.

ITS UNALTERABLE TIDE SWEEPS ALL PEOPLE AND INSTITUTIONS ALONG ITS UNRELENTING PATH. EVERYTHING AND EVERYONE SERVES HISTORY'S SINGLE PURPOSE.

AND WHAT IS THAT PURPOSE?

WHY, TO PRODUCE *ME*, OF COURSE! I'M THE END RESULT OF HISTORY.

YOU?

THINK OF IT! THOUSANDS OF GENERATIONS LIVED AND DIED TO PRODUCE MY EXACT, SPECIFIC PARENTS, WHOSE REASON FOR BEING, OBVIOUSLY, WAS TO PRODUCE *ME*.

ALL HISTORY UP TO THIS POINT HAS BEEN SPENT PREPARING THE WORLD FOR MY PRESENCE.

HMM, 4½ BILLION YEARS PROBABLY WASN'T LONG ENOUGH.

NOW I'M HERE, AND HISTORY IS VINDICATED.

SO NOW THAT HISTORY'S BROUGHT YOU, WHAT ARE YOU GOING TO DO?

OOH, YOU WASCAWWY WABBIT!

CALViN and HobbES

by WATTERSON

CRIICKK

I SURE WISH IT WOULD SNOW.

WHAT'S WITH THE SLED? THERE'S NO SNOW.

I AIM TO FIX *THAT* RIGHT NOW WITH AN APPEAL TO THE SNOW DEMONS.

SNOW DEMONS?

OBVIOUSLY THEY'RE TORMENTING US WITH THIS WIMPY WEATHER BECAUSE THEY'RE ANGRY. WE MUST APPEASE THEM.

OH.

I'M GOING TO LIE HERE ON MY SLED AND THINK SNOW THOUGHTS UNTIL THE SNOW DEMONS HAVE MERCY AND UNLEASH A BLIZZARD.

SNOW, SNOW! HIGH AND LOW! WHEREVER WE GO! LET IT BLOW! TO AND FRO! HI-DE-HO! SNOW! SNOW! SNOW!

WELL, I'LL COME OUT IN EARLY JANUARY AND SEE HOW YOU'RE DOING.

TELL MOM I'LL NEED MY MEALS OUT HERE AND I WON'T BE GOING TO SCHOOL TOMORROW.

CALVIN and HOBBES

by WATTERSON

TRIP!

POOF

POOF

CALVIN? ARE YOU GETTING UP?

MOM AND DAD WON'T BE TOO HAPPY ABOUT *THIS*. NO SIR.

DAD WILL HAVE TO BOLT MY BED TO THE CEILING TONIGHT, AND MOM WILL HAVE TO STAND ON A STEPLADDER TO HAND ME DINNER.

THEN I'LL HAVE TO HOLD MY PLATE UPSIDE-DOWN ABOVE MY HEAD AND SCRAPE THE FOOD OFF THE UNDERSIDE! AND IF I SPILL ANYTHING, IT WILL FLY 10 FEET UP TO THE FLOOR AND SPLOT!

THIS IS GOING TO BE THE MOST FUN I'VE EVER HAD!

ALL THIS WIDE OPEN CEILING SPACE! I WISH I COULD GET MY ROLLER SKATES.

HEY, MAYBE I CAN CLIMB UP THIS BOOKCASE AND WHEN I GET TO THE BOTTOM SHELF, LEAP TO A CHAIR!

THEN I CAN PULL MYSELF ACROSS TO OTHER PIECES OF FURNITURE AND WORK MY WAY TO MY TOY CHEST.

...I CAN HEAR MOM NOW: "HOW ON EARTH DID YOU GET SNEAKER PRINTS ON THE UNDERSIDE OF EACH SHELF?!"

THERE! I THINK I CAN JUMP TO THAT CHAIR AND HANG ONTO THE BACK.

GEERONIMOo°!

¡WHOAA!

WHAM!

GREAT. JUST GREAT.

CALVIN, QUIT BANGING AROUND!

RRG!
MMF!

GETTING ANY *HOMEWORK* DONE, OR ARE YOU JUST RUINING FURNITURE?

MAYBE I'M HANGING HERE FOR DEAR *LIFE!* EVER THINK OF *THAT?*

I'M *TELLING* YOU, MY PERSONAL GRAVITY REVERSED ITS POLARITY! I FALL *UP* NOW!

I'VE BEEN TRAPPED ON THE CEILING! I COULDN'T DO MY HOMEWORK UP *THERE!* MY DESK IS ON THE *FLOOR!*

YOU SHOULD BE GLAD I WASN'T *OUTSIDE* WHEN IT HAPPENED, OR I'D BE SAILING THROUGH THE IONOSPHERE!

RIGHT. NOW I DON'T WANT TO HEAR ANY MORE NONSENSE UNTIL YOU'RE THROUGH WITH YOUR HOMEWORK, UNDERSTAND?

DON'T LET GO! DON'T LET GO!

IT'S... IT'S A MIRACLE! MY PERSONAL GRAVITY IS BACK TO NORMAL!

GLAD TO HEAR IT. NOW DO YOUR MATH.

YOU BET, MOM. BOY, WHAT A RELIEF TO BE PULLED DOWN INSTEAD OF UP!

I'LL CHECK YOUR PROGRESS IN A LITTLE BIT.

UH OH.

THIS HAS BEEN A MOST PECULIAR AFTERNOON.

I'VE GOT TO GET OUTSIDE BEFORE I GROW BIGGER!

I SUPPOSE I SHOULD GET MY PITUITARY GLAND CHECKED.

I KNOW! I'LL RUN DOWNTOWN AND FIND DAD AT WORK! MAYBE HE CAN HELP!

HMM... NOW WHICH BUILDING DOES DAD WORK IN? THEY ALL LOOK THE SAME.

...WELL, MAYBE DAD CAN FIND ME.

calvin and HObbEs by WATTERSON

OUT IN THE FARTHEST REACHES OF THE GALAXY ZOOMS INTERPLANETARY EXPLORER, *SPACEMAN SPIFF!*

OOH, NICE SCENERY!

THE MUCK MONSTERS OF MORDO ARE CLOSING IN ON OUR HERO! A FIERY FLASH OF FATALITY-FLARE MISSES BY MERE MICROMIPS!

SPIFF'S DESPERATE GAMBIT: TO FLY THROUGH THE RINGS OF PLANET ZK-5 BELOW! OUR HERO THROTTLES THE THRUSTERS AND DIVES!

IT WORKS! THE MUCK MONSTERS VEER OFF, AFRAID TO FOLLOW THE FEARLESS SPIFF INTO THE FROZEN FRAGMENTS OF ICE AND ROCK!

SWERVING LEFT, RIGHT, UP, AND DOWN, THE AMAZING SPACEMAN SPIFF PILOTS AROUND EACH HURLING MISSILE! WHAT SKILL! WHAT FORTITU...

POW!

OH NO! OUR HERO IS GOING DOWN!!

Got 'im! Heh heh!

THOSE DARN LITTLE GUYS ARE HARD TO HIT, AREN'T THEY?

I HATE PLAYING "DODGE BALL" IN GYM CLASS.

WHEN ARE WE GOING TO GET A CHRISTMAS TREE?

OH, I DUNNO. PROBABLY A LITTLE AFTER NEW YEAR'S.

AFTER NEW YEAR'S?

SURE. WE CAN JUST GO UP THE STREET AND PICK THE BEST TREE FROM THE NEIGHBORS' DRIVEWAYS.

WHAT?!

SOMETIMES THERE'S STILL TINSEL ON THE TREE TOO, SO YOU DON'T EVEN HAVE TO DECORATE IT! WE'LL SAVE TIME AND MONEY!

OK, WHAT DID YOUR DAD TELL YOU THIS TIME?

YES, CALVIN? YOU HAVE A QUESTION?

YEAH, I WAS WONDERING IF WE COULD STOP THE LESSON HERE AND ADJOURN TO THE PLAYGROUND FOR THE REST OF THE DAY.

OF COURSE NOT. NOW THEN, LET'S ALL TURN TO PAGE 24 AND..

MISS WORMWOOD?

YES?

HOW ABOUT JUST ME THEN?

FOR "SHOW AND TELL" TODAY, I HAVE SOMETHING THAT WILL ASTOUND AND AMAZE YOU! THIS LITTLE GUY CAN...

HAVE YOU ALL HAD YOUR SHOTS?

Calvin and Hobbes

by WATTERSON

DEAR SANTA,
HOW ARE YOU?

WELL, ENOUGH CHIT CHAT.
LET'S GET DOWN TO
BUSINESS.

THIS YEAR I WANT...

WILL YOU DRIVE TO WORK AND FAX MY CHRISTMAS LIST TO SANTA?

THAT'S A BIG ENVELOPE. ARE YOU MAILING A BOOK?

THIS IS MY CHRISTMAS LIST. CAN YOU BELIEVE THIS IS COSTING ME $2.40 TO SEND?

YES.

WELL, AT *THIS* PRICE, ALL I CAN SAY IS THAT SANTA HAD BETTER READ IT DARN CAREFULLY. LAST YEAR I DIDN'T GET HALF OF WHAT I WANTED.

HAVE YOU BEHAVED ANY BETTER THIS YEAR?

IT DEPENDS HOW YOU... *HEY, JUST WHAT ARE YOU INSINUATING?!* WHY, I'LL HAVE YOU KNOW I'VE BEEN A VERITABLE *ANGEL* THIS YEAR, JUST LIKE *ALWAYS!*

IN THAT CASE, WE CAN HAVE A COOKOUT WITH YOUR STOCKING CONTENTS.

DON'T GET SMART, BUB, OR I'LL WALLOP YOU ON THE 26TH.

DID YOU PUT ANYTHING ON YOUR LIST FOR *ME?*

WHAT, AND PAY MORE POSTAGE? THIS PACKAGE IS BREAKING MY ARMS ALREADY! GO WRITE YOUR *OWN* LIST!

TIDINGS OF COMFORT AND JOY TO YOU TOO.

LOOK, IT'S EVERY MAN FOR HIMSELF IN THIS WORLD. NOW GIVE ME A BOOST, WILL YA?

Calvin and Hobbes

by WATTERSON

KNOW WHAT THIS IS?

IT'S A POLAR BEAR BLINKING IN A BLIZZARD! HA HA HA HA!

KNOW WHAT *THIS* IS?

IT SNOWED!

OH MY GOSH, LOOK AT IT ALL! A CREEPING MOUNTAIN OF ICE HAS CRUSHED HALF THE NEIGHBORHOOD!

IT'S A **GLACIER**! RIGHT IN MY OWN TOWN! EVERYTHING NORTH OF HERE HAS BEEN WIPED OFF THE FACE OF THE EARTH! THIS IS **GREAT**!

WOW! WOOLY MAMMOTHS! I'VE NEVER SEEN THOSE BEFORE!

IT'S A NEW ICE AGE! **HOORAYY!!** SLED CITY!

...ONE...LOUSY... HALF...INCH!

LOOK, THE SUN IS COMING OUT!

WHAT ARE YOU DOING STILL IN BED?! I'VE CALLED YOU THREE TIMES! YOU'RE GOING TO MISS THE BUS!

THAT'S THE IDEA. I'M STAYING IN BED UNTIL CHRISTMAS. I WANT TONS OF LOOT THIS YEAR, AND I FIGURE MY CHANCES OF BEING GOOD IMPROVE GREATLY IF I DON'T GET UP.

DISOBEYING YOUR MOTHER AND MISSING THE BUS ISN'T GOOD. IT'S BAD.

THAT DARN SANTA HAS GOT ME EVERY WAY I TURN.

I HATE THIS TIME OF YEAR. I'VE GOT TO BE GOOD FOR TWO MORE WEEKS IF I WANT ANY GOODIES THIS CHRISTMAS! I'LL NEVER MAKE IT.

I *TRY* TO BE GOOD! I *DO!* MY HEART IS AS PURE AS DRIVEN SNOW! IT'S JUST THAT, WELL, SOMETIMES EVENTS BEYOND MY CONTROL CONSPIRE AGAINST ME!

I'M USUALLY AN INNOCENT BYSTAND... HEY, I *SAW* YOU ROLL YOUR EYES! SO YOU DON'T BELIEVE ME, EH?!

ME??

BY GOLLY, EACH OF YOUR EYES WILL BE ROLLING TOWARD THE OTHER WHEN *I'M* THROUGH WITH YOU!

HA! I HOPE YOU ASKED SANTA FOR SOME CRUTCHES!

MISERABLE MISCREANT! QUESTION MY INTEGRITY, WILL YOU?

I CAN'T *QUESTION* IT UNTIL I SEE SOME *EVIDENCE* OF IT!

AUGHH! I'VE BEEN *FIGHTING!*

ONLY IN THE LOOSEST SENSE OF THE WORD.

SANTA, HE *MADE* ME! I DIDN'T *MEAN* TO FIGHT!

YES HE DID! YES HE DID! HE STARTED IT!

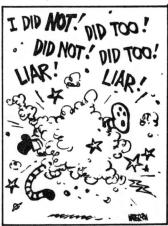

I DID *NOT!* DID TOO! DID NOT! DID TOO! LIAR! LIAR!

LOOK HOBBES, NO ONE *SAW* US FIGHTING, RIGHT? THIS CAN BE *OUR* LITTLE *SECRET*, OK? SANTA DOESN'T HAVE TO KNOW ABOUT THIS, RIGHT?

MAYBE HE DOES AND MAYBE HE DOESN'T.

OK, OK, I'LL EVEN APOLOGIZE! I'M SORRY. HOW'S THAT? SEE, IT'S OK TO FIGHT JUST A LITTLE BIT IF YOU SAY YOU'RE SORRY AFTERWARD.

YOU BIT AND KICKED.

I *SAID* I WAS SORRY! WHAT MORE DO YOU WANT?!

YOU COULD LET ME READ ALL YOUR COMIC BOOKS.

OVER MY DEAD BODY!

"DEAR SANTA, KNOW WHAT CALVIN DID TODAY?"

BOY, IF IT WASN'T SO CLOSE TO CHRISTMAS, I'D POUND YOU GOOD!

YEAH, I'D LIKE TO SEE YOU TRY!

OH NO YOU DON'T! YOU'RE NOT TEMPTING *ME*! I WANT EVERY ITEM ON MY CHRISTMAS LIST, SO I'M BEING *GOOD*, NO MATTER WHAT THE PROVOCATION!

HERE COMES SUSIE DERKINS.

REALLY? QUICK, HELP ME FIND A PINE CONE I CAN THROW AT..

..*NO!* I'M BEING *GOOD!* GOOD! GOOD! GOOD!

YOU'LL NEVER MAKE IT TILL CHRISTMAS. GIVE UP NOW AND ENJOY YOURSELF.

HI CALVIN. ARE YOU BRINGING YOUR STUFFED TIGER TO SCHOOL TODAY?

NO, HE'S JUST KEEPING ME COMPANY WHILE I WAIT FOR THE BUS.

OH.

BUT ACTUALLY, HE'S BEEN NOTHING BUT TROUBLE TODAY. HE'S TRYING TO SABOTAGE MY CHRISTMAS BY MAKING ME BE BAD INSTEAD OF GOOD.

FORTUNATELY, I ASKED SANTA FOR SUCH GREAT PRESENTS THAT I CAN WITHSTAND ANY TEMPTATION. I'M BEING AN ABSOLUTE ANGEL.

WHAT DID YOU ASK FOR?

A HEAT-SEEKING GUIDED MISSILE. I FIGURE FIVE MINUTES WITH ONE OF *THOSE* BABIES WILL MAKE UP FOR THIS WHOLE ROTTEN MONTH.

CALVIN and HOBBES

by WATTERSON

'TIS THE SEASON TO ADVERTISE.

CALVIN, LOOK! YOU GOT A LETTER!

A LETTER? I DIDN'T HEAR THE MAIL TRUCK. A LETTER FOR ME?

THE RETURN ADDRESS SAYS "NORTH POLE".

OH MY GOSH, IT MUST BE FROM *SANTA!* SANTA SENT ME A LETTER! WOW! GEE!

READ IT! READ IT!

"DEAR CALVIN, YOU ROTTEN LITTLE KID..." *OH NO!!* SANTA CALLED ME *ROTTEN!* I'M DOOMED!

KEEP READING.

"I MADE A LIST, BUT I DIDN'T BOTHER CHECKING IT TWICE, BECAUSE OBVIOUSLY YOU'RE THE NAUGHTIEST KID IN THE WHOLE WORLD."

AUGH!

WHAT ELSE?

"I'M WRITING TO GIVE YOU ONE LAST CHANCE. YOU'VE GOT SEVEN DAYS TO GET ON THE 'GOOD BOY' LIST." *SEVEN DAYS!!* OH NO! WHAT CAN I *DO*??

MAYBE HE SAYS.

"I'D SUGGEST YOU START BY BEING KIND TO ANIMALS. PERHAPS YOU KNOW AN ANIMAL WHO WOULD LIKE A SNACK SOON. OR MAYBE YOU SHOULD LET AN ANIMAL READ YOUR COMIC BOOKS SOMETIME. THINK ABOUT IT."

SOUNDS LIKE SAGE ADVICE.

"SIGNED, SANTA CLAWS." *SANTA CLAWS?* WAIT A MINUTE! *I* RECOGNIZE THIS HANDWRITING! IT'S *YOURS!* SANTA DIDN'T WRITE THIS AT ALL!!

GIVE YOU A SNACK, HUH?! HOW ABOUT A KNUCKLE SANDWICH?!

HMPH. WELL, IT'S WHAT SANTA *WOULD'VE* WRITTEN IF HE WASN'T SO BUSY NOW.

WANT TO HELP ME WRITE A BOOK?

SURE. WHAT'S IT ABOUT?

WELL, YOU KNOW WHAT HISTORICAL FICTION IS? THIS IS SORT OF LIKE THAT. I'M WRITING A FICTIONAL AUTOBIOGRAPHY.

IT'S THE STORY OF MY LIFE, BUT WITH A LOT OF PARTS COMPLETELY MADE UP.

WHY WOULD YOU MAKE UP YOUR OWN LIFE?

BECAUSE IN MY BOOK I HAVE A FLAME THROWER!

STILL AND QUIET FELINE FORM, IN THE SUN, ASLEEP AND WARM. HIS TAIL IS LIMP, HIS WHISKERS DROOPED. MAN, WHAT COULD MAKE THIS CAT SO POOPED?

SHEESHH..

HI MOM! I'M MAKING MY OWN NEWSPAPER TO REPORT THE EVENTS OF OUR HOUSEHOLD.

THAT'S NICE.

NOW I'M LOOKING FOR A PAGE ONE LEAD STORY. CAN I INTERVIEW YOU?

SURE.

OK, WHAT ARE YOU CUTTING UP THERE FOR DINNER?

FISH.

KNIFE WIELDING MOTHER HACKS ICHTHYOID! GRIM MELEE IS EVENING RITUAL! SUBURBAN FAMILY DEVOURS VICTIM!

OUT OF THE KITCHEN! OUT! OUT!

HI DAD. I'M MAKING MY OWN NEWSPAPER TO REPORT THE EVENTS OF OUR HOUSEHOLD. WOULD YOU HELP ME OUT?

SURE, WHAT DO YOU NEED?

WELL, YOU CAN TAKE YOUR PICK. EITHER YOU CAN GIVE ME 15 BUCKS TO PAY MY LABOR AND PRODUCTION COSTS...

15 BUCKS?!

...OR YOU CAN BE THE SUBJECT OF A COMIC STRIP CALLED "DOPEY DAD."

SO IN THE NEXT PANEL, DOPEY DAD YELLS, "IT'S BEDTIME FOR *YOU*, YOUNG MAN!"

HEE HEE! LOOK HOW BIG I MADE HIS MOUTH!

OOH HAHH OOH HAHH

OOH HAHH OOH HAHH

OOH HAHH OOH HAHHH

I WISH WE'D GED AD AQUARIUB!

WHAT STORY WOULD YOU LIKE TONIGHT, CALVIN?

HAMSTER HUEY AND THE GOOEY KABLOOIE!

OH NO, NOT *AGAIN!* THAT'S WHAT YOU HEAR *EVERY* NIGHT! LET'S READ SOMETHING DIFFERENT.

I WANT HAMSTER HUEY! I WANT HAMSTER HUEY!

C'MON, WE'LL READ A *NEW* STORY TONIGHT. YOU'LL LIKE IT, I PROMISE.

NO I WON'T! I'LL STAY AWAKE UNTIL MORNING IF YOU DON'T READ HAMSTER HUEY!

I DIDN'T REMEMBER HAMSTER HUEY HAVING QUITE THAT SARCASTIC TONE OF VOICE.

OR DOING EVERYTHING SO *FAST*.

47

Calvin and Hobbes by WATTERSON

Christmas Eve

ON WINDOW PANES, THE ICY FROST
LEAVES FEATHERED PATTERNS, CRISSED & CROSSED,
BUT IN OUR HOUSE THE CHRISTMAS TREE
IS DECORATED FESTIVELY
WITH TINY DOTS OF COLORED LIGHT
THAT COZY UP THIS WINTER NIGHT.
CHRISTMAS SONGS, FAMILIAR, SLOW,
PLAY SOFTLY ON THE RADIO.
POPS AND HISSES FROM THE FIRE
WHISTLE WITH THE BELLS AND CHOIR.
MY TIGER IS NOW FAST ASLEEP
ON HIS BACK AND DREAMING DEEP.
WHEN THE FIRE MAKES HIM HOT,
HE TURNS TO WARM WHATEVER'S NOT.
PROPPED AGAINST HIM ON THE RUG,
I GIVE MY FRIEND A GENTLE HUG.
TOMORROW'S WHAT I'M WAITING FOR,
BUT I CAN WAIT A LITTLE MORE.

49

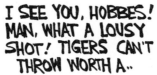
I SEE YOU, HOBBES! MAN, WHAT A LOUSY SHOT! TIGERS CAN'T THROW WORTH A..

SMACK!

I JUST THREW THE FIRST ONE SO YOU'D TURN AROUND.

A NEW DECADE IS COMING UP.

YEAH, BIG DEAL! HMPH.

WHERE ARE THE FLYING CARS? WHERE ARE THE MOON COLONIES? WHERE ARE THE PERSONAL ROBOTS AND THE ZERO GRAVITY BOOTS, HUH? YOU CALL THIS A NEW DECADE?! YOU CALL THIS THE FUTURE?? HA!

WHERE ARE THE ROCKET PACKS? WHERE ARE THE DISINTEGRATION RAYS? WHERE ARE THE FLOATING CITIES?

FRANKLY, I'M NOT SURE PEOPLE HAVE THE BRAINS TO MANAGE THE TECHNOLOGY THEY'VE GOT.

I MEAN, LOOK AT THIS! WE STILL HAVE WEATHER?! GIVE ME A BREAK!

CALVIN and HOBBES by WATTERSON

ARE YOUR PARENTS GOING OUT FOR NEW YEAR'S EVE?

ARE YOU KIDDING?

MY PARENTS' IDEA OF A WILD NIGHT IS TO MIX A SCOOP OF REAL COFFEE IN WITH THE DECAF.

ARE YOU MAKING ANY RESOLUTIONS FOR THE NEW YEAR?

RESOLUTIONS? *ME*?? JUST WHAT ARE YOU IMPLYING? THAT I NEED TO *CHANGE*?? WELL, BUDDY, AS FAR AS *I'M* CONCERNED, I'M PERFECT THE WAY I AM!

FOR YOUR INFORMATION, I'M *STAYING* LIKE THIS, AND EVERYONE ELSE CAN JUST GET *USED* TO IT! IF PEOPLE DON'T LIKE ME THE WAY I AM, WELL, *TOUGH* BEANS! IT'S A FREE COUNTRY! I DON'T NEED ANYONE'S PERMISSION TO BE THE WAY I WANT! THIS IS HOW I AM - TAKE IT OR LEAVE IT!

BY GOLLY, LIFE'S TOO DARN SHORT TO WASTE TIME TRYING TO PLEASE EVERY MEDDLESOME MORON WHO'S GOT AN IDEA HOW I OUGHT TO BE! I DON'T NEED ADVICE! EVERYONE CAN JUST STAY OUT OF MY FACE!

I....

..HOBBES?

HMPH!

HE SHOULD RESOLVE TO BE MORE ATTENTIVE WHEN SOMEONE IS SPEAKING.

WATTERSON

51

BEFORE GOING DOWN A STEEP HILL LIKE THIS, ONE SHOULD ALWAYS GIVE HIS SLED A SAFETY CHECK.

RIGHT.

SEAT BELTS?

NONE.

SIGNALS?

NONE.

BRAKES?

NONE.

STEERING?

NONE.

WHEEEEEE

HOW COLD IS IT OUTSIDE?

I DON'T KNOW. WHY DON'T YOU CHECK?

IT'S PRETTY DARN COLD, I'D SAY.

LET ME SHOW YOU AN INTERESTING GADGET THAT'S HANGING OUTSIDE THE WINDOW.

THIS IS THE PART OF WINTER I LIKE BEST... WHEN YOU COME INSIDE, FREEZING COLD AND SOAKED...

...AND YOU PUT ON FRESH DRY CLOTHES, AND RUN UP TO THE WARM KITCHEN, WHERE MOM'S GOT A STEAMING MUG OF HOT CHOCOLATE WAITING FOR YOU!

MOM?... MOM?? **HEY MOM!**

"CALVIN, I'M NEXT DOOR. DON'T HAVE ANYTHING TO EAT, OR YOU'LL SPOIL YOUR APPETITE. MOM."

IT'S GOING TO BE A LONG, COLD, DARK WINTER.

WHILE *I'M* DOING THIS BRAIN SURGERY, *YOU* CAN MAKE A DONOR AND DO A HEART TRANSPLANT!

FORGET IT, CALVIN. I'M NOT PLAYING WITH YOU ANY MORE.

Calvin and Hobbes

by WATTERSON

HEE HEE HEE HEE

BUT FOR MY OWN EXAMPLE, I'D NEVER BELIEVE ONE LITTLE KID COULD HAVE SO MUCH BRAINS!

I'M A GENIUS, HOBBES. THERE'S SIMPLY NO OTHER WORD FOR IT. WHO ELSE WOULD THINK TO ARM A TOBOGGAN? IT'S JUST GENIUS!

SEE SUSIE DERKINS DOWN THERE? SHE'S BUILDING A SNOWMAN AND DOESN'T EVEN KNOW WE'RE UP HERE! WE'LL ZIP DOWN AND PELT HER SILLY WITH SNOWBALLS!

YOU STEER AND I'LL THROW! SEE, THE SNOWBALLS WILL GAIN EVEN MORE FORCE FROM OUR OWN VELOCITY! GENIUS, HUH?

HA HA! WE'LL BE A MILE AWAY BEFORE SHE CAN EVEN PICK HER HEAD OUT OF THE SNOW!

THERE SHE IS! STEER CLOSER SO I CAN GET HER! LEAN! LEAN!

AUGH! STEER! YOU'RE TOO CLOSE! MAYDAY!!

PIFF!

ANOTHER GENIUS THWARTED BY AN INCAPABLE ASSISTANT.

HEY CALVIN, LOOK UP.

54

LOOK, HOBBES! MY NEWEST INVENTION!

ISN'T THAT YOUR TRANSMOGRIFIER?

IT *WAS*, BUT I MADE SOME MODIFICATIONS. SEE, THE BOX IS ON ITS SIDE NOW. IT'S A DUPLICATOR!

AH.

IT COMBINES THE TECHNOLOGIES OF THE TRANSMOGRIFIER AND A PHOTOCOPIER, SO INSTEAD OF MERELY MAKING A REPRODUCTION ON PAPER, *THIS* MACHINE ACTUALLY CREATES A REAL DUPLICATE!

SO OUR FINANCIAL WORRIES ARE OVER?

AND COUNTERFEITING IS JUST *ONE* OF ITS MANY USES AROUND THE HOME!

DUPLICATOR

HAVE YOU TESTED YOUR DUPLICATOR MACHINE YET?

I WAS JUST ABOUT TO. YOU CAN HELP.

OH BOY! WHAT WILL WE DUPLICATE FIRST?

ME!

YOU??

YEAH! MOM WANTS ME TO CLEAN MY ROOM, SO I'LL DUPLICATE MYSELF AND LET THE DUPLICATE DO THE WORK! SMART, HUH?

I CAN PICTURE THE LOOK ON YOUR PARENTS' FACES WHEN THEY FIND OUT THEY'VE SUDDENLY HAD TWINS.

TWINS, HECK! THIS SUMMER I CAN MAKE A WHOLE BASEBALL TEAM!

OK HOBBES, PRESS THE BUTTON AND DUPLICATE ME.

ARE YOU SURE THIS IS SUCH A GOOD IDEA?

BROTHER! YOU DOUBTING THOMASES GET IN THE WAY OF MORE SCIENTIFIC ADVANCES WITH YOUR STUPID ETHICAL QUESTIONS! THIS IS A *BRILLIANT* IDEA! HIT THE BUTTON, WILL YA?

I'D HATE TO BE ACCUSED OF INHIBITING SCIENTIFIC PROGRESS... HERE YOU GO.

BOINK

BUTTON

SCIENTIFIC PROGRESS GOES "BOINK"?

IT WORKED! IT WORKED! I'M A GENIUS!

NO YOU'RE NOT, YOU LIAR! *I* INVENTED THIS!

BUTTON

DUP

THE DUPLICATOR WORKED! HOBBES, MEET MY DUPLICATE!

OOG, I'M NOT SURE I'M READY FOR THIS.

HEY, NICE ROOM.

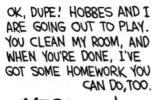
OK, DUPE! HOBBES AND I ARE GOING OUT TO PLAY. YOU CLEAN MY ROOM, AND WHEN YOU'RE DONE, I'VE GOT SOME HOMEWORK YOU CAN DO, TOO.

WHAT?!

FORGET IT, BUB! FIND SOME OTHER SUCKER TO DO YOUR DIRTY WORK! LAST ONE OUTSIDE IS A ROTTEN EGG!

HEY! COME BACK HERE!

HE'S A DUPLICATE OF YOU, ALL RIGHT.

WHAT DO YOU MEAN? THIS GUY IS A TOTAL JERK!

WHERE ARE YOU GOING? DID YOU CLEAN YOUR ROOM LIKE I ASKED YOU TO?

I'M GOING OUTSIDE. CALVIN CAN CLEAN HIS OWN ROOM.

I DON'T WANT ANY NONSENSE, CALVIN. GO UPSTAIRS.

CALVIN? I'M NOT CALVIN. I'M HIS DUPLICATE. CALVIN'S IN HIS ROOM.

WHAT DID I JUST SAY? NO NONSENSE, CALVIN! GO CLEAN YOUR ROOM.

BOY, YOU ARE A CRABBY LADY! WHO ARE YOU? CALVIN'S CRUEL GOVERNESS?

THAT DOES IT.

C'MON, HOBBES. WE'D BETTER GO FIND MY DUPLICATE BEFORE HE GETS ME IN TROUBLE.

I'M TELLING YOU, LADY, YOU'VE GOT THE WRONG GUY! I'M A DUPLICATE OF CALVIN! CALVIN'S IN HIS ROOM!

WE'LL SEE ABOUT THAT. GIVE ME YOUR COAT.

SEE, CALVIN? THERE'S NO ONE HERE. NOW THAT'S ENOUGH GAMES. CLEAN YOUR ROOM, OK?

CALVIN?

I DON'T SEE HIM, HOBBES. MAYBE HE'S OUTSIDE, HUH?

WE'D BETTER HURRY. I THINK I HEAR YOUR MOM COMING DOWN THE STAIRS.

OK DUPLICATES, LISTEN UP. AS LONG AS YOU'RE ALL HERE AND I DON'T KNOW HOW TO GET RID OF YOU, WE MIGHT AS WELL COOPERATE.

SPECIFICALLY, WITH FIVE DUPLICATES, WE CAN DIVIDE UP THE SCHOOL WEEK SO THERE'S ONE DUPLICATE FOR EACH DAY.

IF THE REST OF US LAY LOW, WE CAN TAKE TURNS GOING TO SCHOOL, AND NO ONE WILL BE THE WISER!

GREAT!

NOW THAT STILL LEAVES US WITH THE QUESTION OF WHO GETS THE BED TONIGHT.

WE'LL FIGHT YOU FOR IT.

HI CALVIN.

I'M NOT CALVIN. I'M DUPLICATE NUMBER TWO.

WHAT ARE YOU TALKING ABOUT?

WE DREW STRAWS, AND TODAY'S MY DAY TO GO TO SCHOOL. WE'RE ALL TAKING TURNS SO WE EACH ONLY GO ONCE A WEEK.

CALVIN, YOU ARE SO WEIRD I'M NOT EVEN GOING TO TALK TO YOU.

I'M NOT CALVIN.

I WISH I LIVED SOMEPLACE WHERE I WENT TO A NORMAL BUS STOP.

ARE YOU IN CALVIN'S CLASS? WILL YOU HELP ME FIND HIS LOCKER?

CALVIN, WOULD YOU PLEASE DEMONSTRATE THE HOMEWORK PROBLEM YOU WERE ASSIGNED YESTERDAY?

I WASN'T HERE YESTERDAY.

YES, YOU WERE, CALVIN. DIDN'T YOU DO YOUR PROBLEM?

I'M NOT CALVIN. I'M DUPLICATE NUMBER FIVE. DUPLICATE TWO WAS HERE YESTERDAY, NOT ME. WE'RE ALL TAKING TURNS. NUMBER TWO WILL BE BACK NEXT WEEK, AND YOU CAN ASK HIM TO DO THE PROBLEM THEN.

LOOK, I DON'T SEE WHAT'S SO HARD ABOUT THIS!

PRINCIPAL

WELL, HOBBES, I GUESS WE LEARNED A VALUABLE LESSON FROM THIS DUPLICATING MESS.

AND THAT IS?

AND THAT IS, UM...IT'S THAT, WELL...

OK, SO WE DIDN'T LEARN ANY BIG LESSON. SUE ME.

LIVE AND DON'T LEARN, THAT'S US.

WHAP!

DID YOU THROW THAT?!?

THROW WHAT?

LET ME SEE YOUR MITTENS! *THERE*, LOOK! FLECKS OF BARK, PIECES OF GRAVEL, SPOTS OF MUD, AND GRANULES OF ICE! THAT WAS *YOUR* SNOWBALL, ALL RIGHT!

THAT'S THE PROBLEM WITH HAVING A SIGNATURE STYLE.

HA! YOU MISSED BY A MILE! NYAH NYAHH! THBPTBH!

YES?

YOU'RE DARN LUCKY I DIDN'T GET THAT SNOW-BLOWER FOR CHRISTMAS!

WHOSE BRILLIANT IDEA WAS IT TO TAKE A HIKE OUT IN THIS BITTER COLD?! HOW MUCH LONGER DO WE HAVE TO DO THIS?

I FEEL LIKE I'M IN "DR. ZHIVAGO."

ALL RIGHT, CALVIN. YOU'VE MADE YOUR POINT, I THINK.

I HATE THESE FORCED MARCHES! WHEN ARE WE GOING HOME?

THIS IS JUST A LITTLE WALK, CALVIN. THE EXERCISE IS GOOD FOR YOU.

BUT I'M *FREEZING!* IT MUST BE 80 BELOW! MY TOES ARE NUMB!

NUMB TOES BUILD CHARACTER.

YEAH? WELL, WHAT ABOUT FROSTBITE?! WHAT ABOUT HYPOTHERMIA?! WHAT ABOUT *DEATH?!* I SUPPOSE *THOSE* BUILD CHARACTER TOO! I CAN'T BELIEVE I'M OUT HERE!

THIS IS THE WORST DAY OF MY ENTIRE LIFE! I HATE THIS! AREN'T WE GOING HOME YET? IT SEEMS LIKE WE'VE BEEN WALKING FOR HOURS!

CALVIN, WILL YOU *PLEASE* STOP GRIPING?

GRIPING? *I'M* NOT GRIPING! I'M JUST *OBSERVING* WHAT A MISERABLE EXPERIENCE THIS IS! BUT OK! *SURE!* AS LONG AS I'M TRUDGING HUNDREDS OF MILES FOR NO APPARENT REASON, I MIGHT AS WELL DO IT IN *SILENCE*, RIGHT?!

JUST BECAUSE I'M OUT IN THE ELEMENTS LIKE A COMPLETE IDIOT, WATCHING MY DIGITS TURN TO ICE AND FALL OFF, I SURE AS HECK WOULDN'T EVER WANT TO SPOIL THE...

WE'RE *HOME.*

WE'RE WHAT? OH LOOK, WE'RE HOME!

64

QUIZ:
Jack and Joe leave their homes at the same time and drive toward each other. Jack drives at 60 mph, while Joe drives at 30 mph. They pass each other in 10 minutes.

How far apart were Jack and Joe when they started?

IT WAS ANOTHER BAFFLING CASE. BUT THEN, YOU DON'T HIRE A **PRIVATE EYE** FOR THE **EASY** ONES...

I'D PLANNED TO TAKE THE DAY **OFF** AND SPEND TIME WITH A COUPLE OF **BUDDIES.** MY BUDDIES TRAVEL LIGHT AND THEY'RE FUN TO HAVE AROUND. ONE TRAVELS IN A HOLSTER, AND THE OTHER IN A HIP FLASK.

MY NAME IS **BULLET.** TRACER BULLET. WHAT PEOPLE **CALL** ME IS SOMETHING ELSE AGAIN. I'M A PRIVATE EYE. IT SAYS SO ON MY DOOR.

THE **LAST** THING I WANTED THIS MORNING WAS A **CASE** TO SOLVE, BUT THE DAME WHO BROUGHT IT WAS **PERSUASIVE.** MOST DAMES **ARE,** SOMEHOW.

GET TO WORK, CALVIN.

I TOLD HER IT WOULD COST HER FIFTY GREENBACKS A DAY, PLUS EXPENSES.

I STEPPED OUT INTO THE RAINY STREETS AND REVIEWED THE FACTS. THERE WEREN'T MANY.

TWO SAPS, JACK AND JOE, DRIVE TOWARD EACH OTHER AT 60 AND 30 MPH. AFTER 10 MINUTES, THEY PASS. I'M SUPPOSED TO FIND OUT HOW FAR APART THEY STARTED.

QUESTIONS POUR DOWN LIKE THE RAIN. WHO **ARE** THESE MUGS? WHAT WERE THEY TRYING TO ACCOMPLISH? WHY WAS JACK IN SUCH A HURRY? AND WHAT DIFFERENCE DOES IT MAKE WHERE THEY STARTED FROM??

I HAD A HUNCH THAT, BEFORE THIS WAS OVER, I'D BE SORRY I ASKED.

CALVIN and HOBBES

by WATTERSON

I THINK THIS IS MY FAVORITE TIME OF YEAR! THE NEW SNOW MAKES EVERYTHING LOOK SO PRETTY.

WHOAAAAA! WUMPH!

I THINK THIS IS MY FAVORITE TIME OF YEAR! THE NEW SNOW MUFFLES APPROACHING FOOTSTEPS! HOO HOO!

MAN, I CAN'T WAIT FOR SPRING.

67

Calvin and Hobbes
by WATTERSON

LET'S HURRY DOWN THIS HILL AND GO HOME.

WHAT'S THE RUSH?

THERE'S A TV SHOW ON SLEDDING I WANT TO WATCH.

IN MY OPINION, TELEVISION VALIDATES EXISTENCE.

TAKE THIS SLED RIDE, FOR INSTANCE. THE EXPERIENCE IS FLEETING AND ELUSIVE. BY TOMORROW, WE'LL HAVE FORGOTTEN IT, AND IT MAY AS WELL HAVE NOT EVEN HAPPENED.

BUT IF WE WERE ON TV NOW, COUNTLESS VIEWERS WOULD SHARE IN THE EVENT AND CONFIRM IT! THIS RIDE WOULD BECOME A PART OF MASS CONSCIOUSNESS!

AND ON TV, THE IMPACT OF AN EVENT IS DETERMINED BY THE IMAGE, NOT ITS SUBSTANCE.

SO WITH SOME STRONG VISUALS, OUR SLED RIDE COULD CONCEIVABLY MAKE US CULTURAL ICONS!

INSTEAD OF BEING BORING OL' CALVIN AND HOBBES, WE'D BE "CALVIN AND HOBBES-AS SEEN ON TV"! WOULDN'T THAT BE GREAT? DON'T YOU WISH WE WERE ON TV?

AT THIS MOMENT, I LIKE MY ANONYMITY.

I THINK WE SHOULD GO FOR THE HIGH-BROW PUBLIC TV AUDIENCE, DON'T YOU?

Calvin and Hobbes

by WATTERSON

I LOVE FRESH SNOW.

IT HELPS ME AVOID CALVIN.

WINTER HAS WRAPPED THE LAND IN A SOFT, WHITE BLANKET, AND THE EARTH SLEEPS QUIETLY...

WHOAAOOMPHAA!
LOOK OUT BELOW!
LEAN! LEAN!
NGH!

MAYDAY! BAIL OUT!
YAAA

SMASH!

YOU CALL THAT STEERING? WE ALMOST GOT KILLED! MY FAULT? YEAH, STEP OVER HERE AND SAY THAT, YOU STRIPEY DOPE! THAT'S RIGHT, I'M TALKING TO YOU!

HEY! OW! QUIT BITING!
OOF! TAKE THAT!
OW!
OW!

I THINK WHEN I GROW UP, I'LL LIVE IN THE TROPICS.

QUIT IT! QUIT IT! LET GO!

WHEE! LET'S GET THE SLED OUT OF THE TREE AND DO THAT AGAIN!

YOU KNOW WHAT WE NEED FOR OUR SLED? A SIREN!

WUMP!

ANY DUMB KID CAN BUILD A SNOWMAN, BUT IT TAKES A GENIUS LIKE ME TO CREATE *ART*.

THIS SNOW SCULPTURE TRANSCENDS CORPOREAL LIKENESS TO EXPRESS DEEPER TRUTHS ABOUT THE HUMAN CONDITION! THIS SCULPTURE IS ABOUT GRIEF AND SUFFERING!

ONE LOOK AT THE TORTURED COUNTENANCE OF THIS FIGURE CONFIRMS THAT THE ARTIST HAS DRUNK DEEPLY FROM THE CUP OF LIFE! THIS WORK SHALL ENDURE AND INSPIRE FUTURE GENERATIONS!

STILL MAKING SNOW ART?

YEP!

YESTERDAY YOUR SCULPTURE MELTED.

THIS TIME I'M TAKING *ADVANTAGE* OF MY MEDIUM'S IMPERMANENCE.

THIS SCULPTURE IS ABOUT TRANSIENCE. AS THIS FIGURE MELTS, IT INVITES THE VIEWER TO CONTEMPLATE THE EVANESCENCE OF LIFE. THIS PIECE SPEAKS TO THE HORROR OF OUR OWN MORTALITY!

HEY STUPID! IT'S TOO WARM TO BUILD A SNOWMAN! WHAT A DOPE! HA HA HA HA!

A PHILISTINE ON THE SIDEWALK.

GENIUS IS NEVER UNDERSTOOD IN IT'S OWN TIME.

WHY SHOULD I GO TO SCHOOL?! WHY CAN'T I STAY HOME?

WHY DO I HAVE TO LEARN? WHY CAN'T I STAY THE WAY I AM? WHAT'S THE POINT OF THIS? WHY DO THINGS HAVE TO BE THIS WAY? WHY CAN'T THINGS BE DIFFERENT?

LIFE IS FULL OF MYSTERIES, ISN'T IT? SEE YOU THIS AFTERNOON.

AT 7:00 AM, MOM'S NOT VERY PHILOSOPHICAL.

ALL SET?

YEP!

OK, GET READY!

NOW!

CLICK

SMASH

TOO BAD THE BACK OF THE CAMERA OPENED WHEN WE LANDED. THAT WOULD'VE BEEN A GREAT PICTURE!

HA! I'VE GOT A GREAT WORD AND IT'S ON A "DOUBLE WORD SCORE" BOX!

"ZQFMGB" ISN'T A WORD! IT DOESN'T EVEN HAVE A VOWEL!

IT IS *SO* A WORD! IT'S A WORM FOUND IN NEW GUINEA! EVERYONE KNOWS THAT!

I'M LOOKING IT UP.

YOU DO, AND I'LL LOOK UP THAT 12-LETTER WORD *YOU* PLAYED WITH ALL THE Xs AND Js!

WHAT'S YOUR SCORE FOR ZQFMGB?

957.

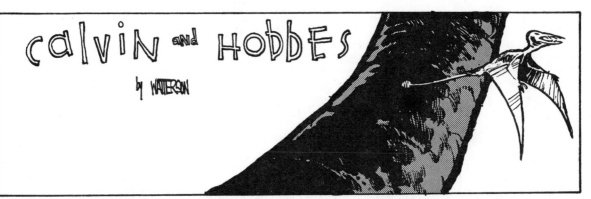

calvin and HObbes
by WATTERSON

140 MILLION YEARS AGO, THE INCREDIBLE 'ULTRASAURS' WANDER THE EARTH! SOME WEIGH OVER 70 TONS, AND EVEN THE VICIOUS ALLOSAURS ARE NO MATCH FOR THESE GIANTS!

BUT WAIT! A DISTANT RUMBLING SENDS THE ULTRASAURS INTO A PANICKED STAMPEDE! IS IT A VOLCANO? IS IT AN EARTHQUAKE?

NO! IT'S.. IT'S A *CALVINOSAURUS!*

NAMED AFTER THE RENOWNED PALEONTOLOGIST WHO DISCOVERED IT, THE HUGE CALVINOSAUR CAN EAT AN ULTRASAUR IN A SINGLE BITE!

PHOOEY! I NEVER FIND *ANYTHING.*

IT LOOKS LIKE YOU'VE HIT THE SEWER PIPE.

OK HOBBES, TOSS UP THIS DECK OF CARDS, AND I'LL PLUG THE ACE OF SPADES!

OH BOY, A SHOOTING TRICK!

GO!

BLAM BAM POW ZING BLOOIE BANG

HERE IT IS! WOW! SIX CLEAN HOLES THROUGH THE ACE!

PRETTY GOOD, HUH? WANT TO KNOW HOW I DID IT? I USED A HOLE PUNCHER AHEAD OF TIME!

HMM, ON SECOND THOUGHT, I'LL FOLD.

HEY, WHAT'S WITH THIS DECK?!

THIS MORNING I HAD A WONDERFUL DREAM. BY HOLDING MY ARMS OUT STIFF AND PUSHING DOWN HARD, I FOUND I COULD SUSPEND MYSELF A FEW FEET ABOVE THE GROUND. I FLAPPED HARDER, AND SOON I WAS SOARING EFFORTLESSLY OVER THE TREES AND TELEPHONE POLES! I COULD *FLY!* I FOLDED MY ARMS BACK AND ZOOMED LOW OVER THE NEIGHBORHOOD. EVERYONE WAS AMAZED, AND THEY RAN ALONG UNDER ME AS I SHOT BY. THEN I ROCKETED UP SO FAST THAT MY EYES WATERED FROM THE WIND. I LAUGHED AND LAUGHED, MAKING HUGE LOOPS ACROSS THE SKY! ..THAT'S WHEN MOM WOKE ME UP AND SAID I WAS GOING TO MISS THE BUS IF I DIDN'T GET MY BOTTOM OUT OF BED; 20 MINUTES LATER, HERE I AM, STANDING IN THE COLD RAIN, WAITING TO GO TO SCHOOL, AND I JUST REMEMBERED I FORGOT MY LUNCH.

TUESDAYS DON'T START MUCH WORSE THAN THIS.

I DID IT! I DID IT!

SOMEHOW I IMAGINED THIS EXPERIENCE WOULD BE MORE REWARDING.

HEWWO! IS HOBBESIE-WOBBSIE SWEEPY? OOH, HE'S JUST A BIG SNOOGIE-WOOGIE, ISN'T HE? YES HE *IS!* HEWWO, SNOOGIE-WOOGIE!

GLOMP! HEY! HEY!

OW! LEGGO, YOU BLOODTHIRSTY CARNIVORE! OW! OW! OW!

I CAN SEE WHY LITTLE TABBY CATS ARE SO MUCH MORE POPULAR.

ONCE UPON A TIME, THERE WAS A...

HOLD IT.

YOU KNOW WHAT *I'D* LIKE TO SEE? I'D LIKE TO SEE THE THREE BEARS EAT THE THREE LITTLE PIGS, AND THEN THE BEARS JOIN UP WITH THE BIG BAD WOLF AND EAT GOLDILOCKS AND LITTLE RED RIDING HOOD!

TELL ME A STORY LIKE *THAT,* OK?

AND HOW SHOULD HANSEL AND GRETEL MEET *THEIR* UNTIMELY DEMISE?

THE WITCH EATS THEM AND THEN THE WOLF EATS THE WITCH.

HEY DAD, CAN I TAKE THE GAS CAN FOR THE LAWN MOWER OUT IN THE BACK YARD?

WHAT ON EARTH FOR? IT'S 8:00 AT NIGHT!

I WANT TO POUR GASOLINE IN BIG LETTERS ON THE LAWN...

.. AND SET FIRE TO IT SO AIRPLANES CAN READ IT AS THEY FLY OVER!

NO, YOU CAN'T DO THAT! DON'T BE RIDICULOUS!

I DON'T EVEN WANT TO KNOW WHAT HE INTENDED TO WRITE.

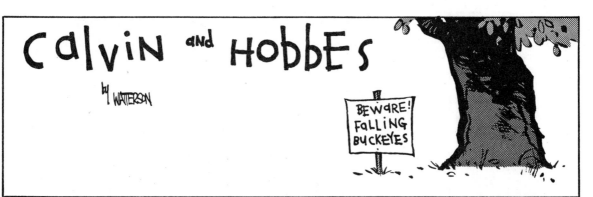

CALVIN and HOBBES

by WATTERSON

BEWARE! FALLING BUCKEYES

HERE COMES SOMEBODY!

THIS MEETING OF THE TOP SECRET CLUB G.R.O.S.S. (GET RID OF SLIMY GIRLS) WILL COME TO ORDER. TODAY THIS AUGUST ASSEMBLY WILL DECIDE WHETHER TO DEMOTE PRESIDENT HOBBES ON CHARGES OF HERESY!

HERESY?!

LET THE RECORD SHOW THAT THE DEFENDANT MADE AN UNDISPARAGING COMMENT ABOUT THE POSSIBLE MEMBERSHIP OF SUSIE DERKINS, AN ADMITTED GIRL AND ENEMY OF THIS CLUB.

LET THE RECORD ALSO SHOW THAT SUPREME DICTATOR-FOR-LIFE CALVIN IS A NINCOMPOOP.

OK, JUST FOR THAT, YOU'RE ALSO CHARGED WITH INSUBORDINATION! THIS COURT FINDS YOU GUILTY ON BOTH COUNTS AND STRIPS YOU OF YOUR TITLE!

HA! AS COURT STENOGRAPHER, I REFUSE TO ENTER THE VERDICT! IN FACT, I'M PROMOTING MYSELF TO "EL TIGRE NUMERO UNO"!

OH YEAH?! WELL THEN, I PROMOTE MYSELF TO "MOST HIGHEST, GRANDEST, EXALTED, UM, SUPREME, UH..."

THERE! I WROTE "HOBBES EQUALS GREAT" IN THE OFFICIAL CLUB NOTEBOOK! NOW IT'S A LAW!

IT IS NOT! GIMME THAT!

HOBS = GRAT

HA HA HA! I'M WRITING "HOBBES EQUALS UGLY FUR BALL"! WHAT DO YOU THINK OF THAT?

OH HO! I TAKE THE SUPREME DICTATOR HAT! NOW I'M THE SUPREME DICTATOR!

YOU GIVE THAT BACK!

I DECLARE YOU NULL AND VOID!

TRUCE?

TRUCE.

WHAT A GREAT CLUB. TOO BAD WE DON'T HAVE MORE MEMBERS.

MAYBE WE SHOULD ALLOW SUSIE TO JOIN.

DO YOU... I MEAN, DOES *HOBBES* WANT ANY TUNA FISH THIS WEEK?

NO, HOBBES STOPPED EATING CANNED TUNA. YOU KNOW, THEY KILL DOLPHINS TO GET IT.

OK, I'LL PUT IT BACK.

SO WHAT DOES HOBBES LIKE NOW INSTEAD?

FRESH SWORDFISH STEAKS. HE LIKES THEM GRILLED OUTSIDE.

MM-HMM. HOW ABOUT PEANUT BUTTER?

HERE'S SOME CLEAN CLOTHES. WILL YOU PUT THEM AWAY PLEASE?

HEY, MY UNDERWEAR ISN'T PRESSED! NEITHER ARE MY SOCKS! YOU DIDN'T FINISH IRONING!

BUDDY, IF YOU WANT YOUR UNDERWEAR IRONED, YOU CAN DO IT YOURSELF!

WHAT KIND OF MOTHER *ARE* YOU?!

SHE SHOULD TAKE MORE PRIDE IN HER WORK.

I ASKED MOM IF I WAS A GIFTED CHILD. ...SHE SAID THEY CERTAINLY WOULDN'T HAVE *PAID* FOR ME.

YOU CAN RELATE THIS LITTLE STORY WHEN THE REPORTERS ASK HOW I WENT BAD.

MOM! HOBBES IS READING MY COMIC BOOKS! TELL HIM TO STOP!

I TOLD HIM TO GO BUY HIS OWN, AND HE *SNARLED* AT ME! MAKE HIM GIVE 'EM BACK!

MAYBE YOU SHOULD BE GLAD HE'S MORE LITERATE THAN MOST STUFFED ANIMALS.

BUT THEY'RE *MY* COMIC BOOKS, NOT *HIS*!

WELL, YOU SHOULD LEARN TO SHARE. I DON'T THINK HOBBES WILL HURT THEM.

ARE YOU KIDDING?! HE DREW A MUSTACHE AND GLASSES ON EVERY PICTURE OF NUKE-MAN LAST ISSUE! IN *PEN*!

WHY DON'T YOU GO PLAY OUTSIDE, CALVIN.

HOW'S YOUR MATH COMING?

I DON'T *DO* MATH ANY MORE. I DECIDED I'M MORE OF A "VISUAL" PERSON.

GOOD. VISUALIZE BEING THE ONLY 45-YEAR-OLD IN FIRST GRADE.

VISUALIZING A FEW SUMS NOW, EH?

ACTUALLY, I'M VISUALIZING *YOU* IN TRACTION. HELP ME DO THESE, OK?

HEY HOBBES, I'LL GIVE YOU 20 QUESTIONS TO GUESS WHAT I HAVE IN MY HANDS, OK?

OK. IS IT LOATHSOME?

YES!

IS IT SOME BIG CENTIPEDE WITH POISON PINCHERS?

CENTIPEDES HAVE POISON PINCHERS?

I THINK SO.

MAN, IT'S A GOOD THING YOU GUESSED IT SO FAST!

WITH YOU, IT'S NEVER TOO DIFFICULT.

84

I GET THE FEELING THERE WAS NO RIGHT ANSWER TO THAT QUESTION.

I SURE LIKE CHOCOLATE FROSTED SUGAR BOMBS! LOOK HOW BROWN THE MILK GETS!

UGH.

WANT TO SEE SOMETHING WEIRD? LOOK AT THE NUTRITIONAL INFORMATION ON THE BACK PANEL.

WOW. 100% OF THE DAILY RECOMMENDED ALLOWANCE OF CAFFEINE!

HEY LOOK! YOU CAN SEND AWAY FOR A CHOCOLATE FROSTED SUGAR BOMBS "BUZZY THE HUMMINGBIRD" DOLL!

EENIE, MEENIE, MINEY, MOE! CATCH A TIGER BY THE TOE!

IF HE HOLLERS, UM... UH... ..HEH HEH...

WHO WRITES THESE DUMB THINGS ANYWAY?

COUNTY LIBRARY? YES, DO YOU HAVE ANY BOOKS ON HOMEMADE BOMBS?

THAT'S WHAT I SAID. I NEED A BOOK THAT LISTS SUPPLIES AND GIVES STEP-BY-STEP INSTRUCTIONS FOR BUILDING, RIGGING, AND DETONATING THEM.

WELL WHAT ABOUT YOUR OTHER BRANCHES? DON'T THEY HAVE ANY BOOKS LIKE THAT?

BOY, AND PEOPLE WONDER WHY KIDS DON'T READ.

CALVIN and HOBBES

by WATTERSON

ISN'T THIS A NICE WAY TO SPEND THE EVENING? WE SHOULD DO THIS MORE OFTEN.

I STILL THINK ONE OF YOU BROKE THE RABBIT EARS ON PURPOSE.

IT'S GETTING LATE, CALVIN. YOU'D BETTER HEAD UP TO BED.

BUT I'M NOT TIRED! CAN'T I READ A LITTLE MORE?

I DON'T THINK SO.. YOU SEE, WE DON'T WANT YOU TO GET TOO SMART.

YOU DON'T?

HA HA! OF COURSE NOT! IF YOU WERE SMARTER, YOU MIGHT REALIZE..

..YOUR "PARENTS" ARE REALLY BUG-EYED ALIENS FROM NEPTUNE!

HA HA HA

AUGH!!

LET ME GO! LET ME GO!

GOT THE BATTER READY?

YEP! LET'S DUNK THE KID!

M-MM! THERE'S NOTHING LIKE A FRESH BATCH OF EARTH BOY WAFFLES!

WAFFLES? HELP! HELP!

EEP!

POOF

I WASN'T ASLEEP! I'M NOT TIRED!

LOOK, HIS FACE WAS PUSHED INTO YOUR LEG SO HARD, IT LEFT CORDUROY LINES!

Z

THIS IS AWFUL! IF WE STEP OUT OF LINE *ONCE* TONIGHT, ROSALYN WILL KILL US, AND THEN MOM AND DAD WILL KILL US AGAIN WHEN THEY GET HOME.

I GUESS THAT'S THAT.

WHAT?! ADMIT DEFEAT? *NEVER!*

THINGS MAY LOOK GRIM FOR *US,* BUT *NOTHING* IS GRIM FOR...

...*STUPENDOUS MAN!* CHAMPION OF LIBERTY! FOE OF TYRANNY!

I'M GOING TO GET IN BED NOW AND AVOID THE RUSH.

A BOLT OF FIERY CRIMSON STREAKS ACROSS THE SKY! IT'S *STUPENDOUS MAN!*

THE FIENDISH *BABY SITTER GIRL* HAS A LOCAL HOUSEHOLD IN HER IRON GRIP OF TERROR! THE MAN OF MEGA-MIGHT ZOOMS TO THE RESCUE!

I'M IN LUCK! BABY SITTER GIRL IS MOMENTARILY DISTRACTED!

HI CHARLIE, IT'S ROSALYN. YEAH, I'M OVER AT THE LITTLE MONSTER'S HOUSE AGAIN. HMM? NO, ACTUALLY HE'S BEEN PRETTY GOOD TONIGHT. YEAH, I CAN'T BELIEVE IT.

ANYWAY CHARLIE, I'M SORRY WE COULDN'T GO OUT TONIGHT, BUT THIS LITTLE CREEP'S PARENTS ARE SO DESPERATE TO GET AWAY FROM HIM ONCE IN A WHILE THAT THEY...

YAHH! FREEDOM AND JUSTICE SHALL ALWAYS PREVAIL OVER TYRANNY, BABY SITTER GIRL!

GET OFF ME, CALVIN, YOU PEST! OW! LET GO! QUIT IT!

STUPENDOUS MAN HAS THE STRENGTH OF A MILLION MORTAL MEN! GIVE UP!

LISTEN CHARLIE, I'M GOING TO HAVE TO CALL YOU BACK. YOU WOULDN'T BELIEVE WHAT THIS CRETIN IS WEARING.

WITH MUSCLES OF MAGNITUDE, *STUPENDOUS MAN* FIGHTS WITH HEROIC RESOLVE!

OK CALVIN, YOU WANT TO PLAY ROUGH, HUH?

GREAT MOONS OF NEPTUNE! SHE MUST HAVE SUPER POWERS TOO!

YOU'VE GOT *TWO* SECONDS TO GET YOUR CAPED BUTT IN BED, OR I'LL PUT IT THERE FOR GOOD!

OH NO! THE EVIL AMAZON IS USING SOME PSYCHO-BEAM TO WEAKEN MY STUPENDOUS WILL!

I'M COUNTING! *ONNNNE..*

GASP I... I... MUST RESIST!

TWO!

IN A VERMILLION FLASH, *STUPENDOUS MAN* IS IN THE AIR!

WITH STUPENDOUS SPEED, *STUPENDOUS MAN* IS OUT THE DOOR!

ALL RIGHT, CALVIN! WHERE'D YOU GO?! I KNOW YOU'RE OUT HERE!

YOUR PARENTS TOLD YOU TO *BEHAVE* TONIGHT, REMEMBER?! THEY'RE NOT GOING TO BE HAPPY WHEN THEY HEAR ABOUT *THIS!*

SEE, IF WE HAD BOUGHT A DOG INSTEAD, LIKE *I* WANTED, WE COULD GO OUT LIKE THIS ALL THE TIME.

HONEY, WE CAME HERE TO RELAX. LET'S TALK ABOUT SOMETHING ELSE.

THERE IS NO WAY I'M GETTING PAID ENOUGH FOR THIS KIND OF AGGRAVATION. HOW COULD A KID WITH SUCH LITTLE LEGS GO SO FAST?!

SECURE IN HIS SECRET FORTRESS, *STUPENDOUS MAN* PLANS HIS STRATEGY! BABY SITTER GIRL IS NO MATCH FOR *STUPENDOUS MAN'S* STUPENDOUS INTELLECT!

CALVIN, YOU'RE IN BIG TROUBLE IF YOU DON'T COME OUT!

YOU MADE IT BACK ALIVE!

OF COURSE! I MADE A STUPENDOUS DASH AS SOON AS ROSALYN WENT AROUND THE HOUSE! SHE *STILL* DOESN'T KNOW WHERE I AM!

THERE GOES ROSALYN AROUND THE HOUSE AGAIN. SHE STILL DOESN'T KNOW YOU SNEAKED BACK INSIDE.

NOW I'LL CHANGE BACK INTO MY SECRET IDENTITY ALTER EGO!

UH OH. SHE SAW THE LIGHT ON IN THIS ROOM. SHE'S COMING IN!

QUICK! GET IN THE COVERS! PRETEND WE'VE JUST BEEN READING IN BED!

BUT SHE KNOWS YOU ATTACKED HER AND RAN OUTSIDE HALF AN HOUR AGO!

THAT WAS *STUPENDOUS MAN,* NOT MILD-MANNERED CALVIN! *I'VE* BEEN IN BED WITH MY PJs ON SINCE 8:00.

YOU THINK SHE'S GOING TO BELIEVE *THAT?*

MY COVERS ARE HERE. MY PAJAMAS ARE *HERE.* IT'S AS PLAIN AS CAN BE!

ALL RIGHT! I FOUND YOU!

FOUND?? WHY, WHAT DO YOU MEAN? I'VE BEEN IN BED READING ALL EVENING WITH HOBBES.

DON'T GIVE ME THAT! YOU JUST NOW SNEAKED INSIDE, TOOK OFF YOUR SILLY COSTUME, AND JUMPED IN BED! I KNOW WHAT YOU DID! WELL YOU'RE GONNA GET IT *NOW,* BUCKO!

OH YEAH? WHAT ARE YOU GOING TO DO TO ME, HUH? YOU CAN'T SEND ME TO BED WHEN I'M ALREADY *IN* BED! SORRY TO SPOIL YOUR FUN, YOU EEL!

OK. DOWNSTAIRS! *MARCH!*

HEY, YOU CAN'T TAKE ME *OUT* OF BED! I NEED MY *SLEEP!* HEY! HEY!

WHILE YOUR DAD IS TAKING ROSALYN HOME, PERHAPS *YOU'D* LIKE TO EXPLAIN WHAT HAPPENED TONIGHT.

GOSH MOM, WHAT'S TO TELL? AT 8:00, I PUT ON MY PAJAMAS, BRUSHED MY TEETH AND WENT STRAIGHT TO BED. NOTHING HAPPENED.

AND THIS?

UH... *LIES!* ALL LIES! ROSALYN MADE ME DO THAT JUST SO I'D GET IN TROUBLE! SHE HATES KIDS! NONE OF THAT IS TRUE! I WENT STRAIGHT TO BED!

NICE TRY, PINOCCHIO.

WELL WHO WOULD'VE THOUGHT ROSALYN WOULD MAKE ME WRITE A FULL CONFESSION?!

NO TV FOR A WEEK! WHAT INJUSTICE!

THEY THINK THEY'VE WON, BUT THEY HAVEN'T!

I'LL SHOW 'EM! I *REFUSE* TO LEARN A LESSON!

I'M INDOMITABLE! THEY CAN'T CHANGE ME!

I'LL SIT IN FRONT OF THE TV ALL WEEK EVEN IF I CAN'T TURN IT ON!

DAD, WILL YOU EXPLAIN THE THEORY OF RELATIVITY TO ME? I DON'T UNDERSTAND WHY TIME GOES SLOWER AT GREAT SPEED.

IT'S BECAUSE YOU KEEP CHANGING TIME ZONES. SEE, IF YOU FLY TO CALIFORNIA, YOU GAIN THREE HOURS ON A FIVE-HOUR FLIGHT, RIGHT?

SO IF YOU GO AT THE SPEED OF LIGHT, YOU GAIN *MORE* TIME, BECAUSE IT DOESN'T TAKE AS LONG TO GET THERE. OF COURSE, THE THEORY OF RELATIVITY ONLY WORKS IF YOU'RE GOING WEST.

GEE, THAT'S NOT WHAT MOM SAID AT **ALL**! SHE MUST BE TOTALLY OFF HER ROCKER.

WELL, WE MEN ARE BETTER AT ABSTRACT REASONING. GO TELL HER THAT.

MOM, CAN WE GO OUT TO THE HIGHWAY?

DO WHAT?

SEE, I'LL PUT ON MY ROLLER SKATES AND TIE A ROPE FROM THE CAR BUMPER TO MY WAIST. THEN WHEN I GIVE YOU THE HIGH FIVE, YOU PATCH OUT WHILE I RIDE BEHIND AT 55 MPH!

WHAT DO YOU SAY? CAN WE GO?

I SURE WISH *YOU* COULD DRIVE.

ACE PILOT SPACEMAN SPIFF CRUISES LOW OVER THE PLANET AT HIGH SPEED!

I WONDER WHAT THIS "E" ON THE FUEL GAUGE MEANS.

THE INTREPID SPACEMAN SPIFF LANDS ON PLANET GORZARG-5!

OUR HERO SETS OFF ACROSS THE DESOLATE TERRAIN IN SEARCH OF HELP! IN THE DISTANCE, METHANE CLOUDS RAIN SODIUM HYDROXIDE, A CAUSTIC ALKALI!

OH NO! THE DOWNPOUR WAS TOO HEAVY FOR THE GROUND TO ABSORB! A STEAMING RIVER OF CORROSIVE LIQUID RUSHES TOWARD OUR HERO!

THE BRAVE SPACEMAN SPIFF SCRAMBLES TO HIGHER GROUND, BUT THE FLOOD CONTINUES TO RISE!

OUR HERO IS TRAPPED! IT'S ONLY A MATTER OF TIME UNTIL THE FOAMING, NOXIOUS WASH CLEANS THE MEAT FROM SPIFF'S BONES! HOW COULD THINGS EVER GET WORSE?!

AUGHH! AN ALIEN COMES TO PUSH HIM IN!

FOR HEAVEN'S SAKE, CALVIN! JUST GET IN!

Hey, lookit the sissy who didn't sign up for recess baseball!

I'M NOT A SISSY!

Oh yeah? You'd rather play dolls on the playground with girls.

I WASN'T PLAYING WITH DOLLS!

Sure you weren't! Let me see your Barbie doll, you sissy wimp!

I'M NOT A WIMP! IN FACT, I WAS GOING TO THE OFFICE TO SIGN UP FOR BASEBALL RIGHT NOW!

THEN AGAIN, IF I'M NOT A WIMP, WHY AM I TAKING THE PATH OF LEAST RESISTANCE?

OFFICE

I SIGNED UP TO PLAY BASEBALL EVERY RECESS, AND I DON'T EVEN *LIKE* BASEBALL THAT MUCH.

I MEAN, IT'S FUN PLAYING BASEBALL WITH JUST *YOU*, BECAUSE WE BOTH GET TO PITCH, BAT, RUN AND CATCH ALL AT ONCE. WE GET TO *DO* EVERYTHING.

MOSTLY WE JUST ARGUE OVER THE RULES WE MAKE UP! THAT'S THE PART *I* LIKE!

BUT THIS WILL BE WITH *TEAMS* AND ASSIGNED POSITIONS AND AN UMPIRE! IT'S *BORING* PLAYING IT THE *REAL* WAY!

DO YOU EVEN KNOW *HOW* TO PLAY THE REAL WAY?

SEE, THAT'S *ANOTHER* PROBLEM! SUPPOSE THEY MAKE ME A HALFBACK. CAN I TACKLE THE SHORTSTOP OR NOT?

I HEAR YOU SIGNED UP TO PLAY SOFTBALL AT RECESS.

YEAH, BUT I DIDN'T EVEN WANT TO. I JUST DID IT TO STOP GETTING TEASED.

WELL, SPORTS ARE GOOD FOR YOU. THEY TEACH TEAMWORK AND COOPERATION. YOU LEARN HOW TO WIN GRACIOUSLY AND ACCEPT DEFEAT. IT BUILDS CHARACTER.

EVERY TIME I'VE BUILT CHARACTER, I'VE REGRETTED IT! I DON'T *WANT* TO LEARN TEAMWORK! I DON'T *WANT* TO LEARN ABOUT WINNING AND LOSING! HECK, I DON'T EVEN WANT TO *COMPETE*! WHAT'S WRONG WITH JUST HAVING FUN BY YOURSELF, HUH?!

WHEN YOU GROW UP, IT'S NOT ALLOWED.

ALL THE MORE REASON I SHOULD DO IT *NOW*!

Panel 1: I SEE YOU'RE BRINGING A GLOVE TODAY. DID YOU SIGN UP FOR RECESS BASEBALL? — YEAH, DON'T REMIND ME.

Panel 2: YOU'RE LUCKY THAT *GIRLS* DON'T HAVE TO PUT UP WITH THIS NONSENSE. IF A *GIRL* DOESN'T WANT TO PLAY SPORTS, THAT'S FINE!

Panel 3: BUT IF A *GUY* DOESN'T SPEND HIS AFTERNOONS CHASING SOME STUPID BALL, HE'S CALLED A WIMP! YOU GIRLS HAVE IT EASY!

Panel 4: ON THE OTHER HAND, *BOYS* AREN'T EXPECTED TO SPEND THEIR LIVES 20 POUNDS UNDERWEIGHT. AND IF YOU DON'T PLAY SPORTS, YOU DON'T GET TO MAKE BEER COMMERCIALS!

Panel 5: MR. LOCKJAW? I'M CALVIN. I'M SUPPOSED TO BE ON TEAM FIVE NOW. — OH YES, YOU'RE THE ONE WHO SIGNED UP LATE. HMM... OK, YOU GO PLAY LEFT FIELD.

Panel 6: LEFT FIELD. OK, I KNOW THAT. LET'S SEE, IF I'M *HERE*, THEN LEFT FIELD WOULD BE... — THAT WAY. PLAY *DEEP* LEFT FIELD.

Panel 7: I GUESS THIS IS PRETTY DEEP.

Panel 8: I THINK BASEBALL IS THE MOST BORING GAME IN THE WORLD. I'VE BEEN STANDING OUT HERE IN DEEP LEFT FIELD ALL THIS TIME, AND NOT A SINGLE BALL HAS COME OUT HERE!

Panel 9: ACTUALLY, I SUPPOSE THAT'S JUST AS WELL. I DON'T KNOW WHAT BASE TO THROW TO ANYWAY. IN FACT, I'M NOT EVEN SURE I CAN THROW THAT FAR.

Panel 10: HEY, WHAT'S EVERYONE DOING? ARE PEOPLE SWITCHING TEAMS, OR WHAT? THE GUYS AT BAT ARE NOW OUT *HERE*!

Panel 11: WELL, I'M SURE SOMEONE WOULD TELL ME IF I WAS SUPPOSED TO BE DOING ANYTHING DIFFERENT.

Row 1

OUR HERO, THE FEARLESS SPACEMAN SPIFF, IS MAROONED ON THE MOST DISTANT PLANET IN THE GALAXY!

THERE'S NO HOPE OF RESCUE FROM THIS BLEAK AND ISOLATED WORLD!

OH, WHAT A DESOLATE PLACE TO BE TRAPPED! SPIFF TRIES DESPERATELY TO REPAIR HIS DISABLED SPACECRAFT!

CRACK

HIGH FLY TO LEFT FIELD! WHO'S OUT THERE?!

OUR HERO PAUSES. THERE'S SOME COMMOTION ON THE HORIZON. *ALIENS!* SPIFF GRABS HIS BLASTER!

Row 2

WHERE'S THE LEFT — FIELDER?!

SOMEBODY CATCH IT!

LEFT FIELD?! HEY, THAT'S *ME!*

WOW! A HIGH FLY RIGHT TO ME! I GOT IT! I GOT IT!

I CAUGHT IT!!

HE CAUGHT IT! IT'S AN OUT!

WAP!

I'M JUST A NATURAL ATHLETE, I GUESS.

HEY, WHO'S *HE?*

ISN'T HE ON THE OTHER TEAM?

Row 3

HEY, LOOK WHO MADE THE OUT!

IT'S *CALVIN!*

HECK, IT WAS NOTHING, GUYS. WHEN YOU'RE IN TOP PHYSICAL CONDITION LIKE ME, YOU CAN...

YOU MORON! WHAT WERE YOU DOING IN THE OUTFIELD?! IT'S A NEW INNING! WE'RE UP TO *BAT!*

HUH?

YOU CAUGHT THE BALL FOR THE WRONG TEAM! YOU GOT OUR OWN GUY OUT! WHAT A DWEEB! WHAT A JERK! WHAT AN *IDIOT!*

OOPS, I DROPPED THE CATCH. IT DOESN'T COUNT NOW, RIGHT?

GET HIM OFF OUR TEAM, MR. LOCKJAW!

CAN I HIT HIM WITH THE BAT? PLEASE? PLEASE??

HEY STUPID, IF YOU'RE GOING TO GET OUR GUYS OUT, WHY DON'T YOU JOIN THE OTHER TEAM?!

WHAT WERE YOU DOING IN THE OUTFIELD? DON'T YOU EVEN KNOW HOW TO PLAY?!

C'MON GUYS, IT'S JUST A GAME! THIS IS SUPPOSED TO BE FUN!

GAMES ARE ONLY FUN WHEN YOU WIN, BONEHEAD! YOU'RE GONNA MAKE US LOSE!

IF YOU SCREW UP AGAIN, YOU'RE DEAD MEAT, CALVIN!

WHO TAUGHT YOU HOW TO PLAY ANYWAY? YOUR GRANDMOTHER?

WAIT TILL I TELL THE OTHER TEAMS ABOUT THIS!

MR. LOCKJAW, I DON'T WANT TO PLAY ANY MORE. THERE'S TOO MUCH TEAM SPIRIT.

OK, QUITTER! GOODBYE.

I DON'T UNDERSTAND IT, HOBBES.

THE KIDS TEASED ME WHEN I DIDN'T PLAY BASEBALL. THEN THEY YELLED AT ME WHEN I DID PLAY. THEN THE TEACHER CALLED ME A "QUITTER" WHEN I STOPPED PLAYING.

UNLESS YOU'RE A STAR, YOU CAN'T PLEASE ANYONE.

IN THAT CASE, WHY NOT JUST PLEASE YOURSELF?

BECAUSE MOM WON'T LET ME MOVE TO MADAGASCAR.

IT'S SATURDAY! WHAT DO YOU WANT TO DO?

ANYTHING BUT PLAY AN ORGANIZED SPORT.

WANT TO PLAY CALVINBALL?

YEAH!

NO SPORT IS LESS ORGANIZED THAN CALVINBALL!

NEW RULE! NEW RULE! IF YOU DON'T TOUCH THE 30-YARD BASE WICKET WITH THE FLAG, YOU HAVE TO HOP ON ONE FOOT!

FASTER! FASTER!

THE TURBO IS POOPED.

THAT'S OK. GRAVITY JUST KICKED IN.

EVER NOTICE HOW DECISIONS MAKE CHAIN REACTIONS?

HOW SO?

WELL, EACH DECISION WE MAKE DETERMINES THE RANGE OF CHOICES WE'LL FACE NEXT.

TAKE THIS FORK IN THE ROAD FOR INSTANCE. WHICH WAY SHOULD WE GO? ARBITRARILY, I CHOOSE LEFT.

NOW, AS A DIRECT RESULT OF THAT DECISION, WE'RE FACED WITH ANOTHER CHOICE: SHOULD WE JUMP THIS LEDGE OR RIDE ALONG THE SIDE OF IT?

IF WE HADN'T TURNED LEFT AT THE FORK, THIS NEW CHOICE WOULD NEVER HAVE COME UP.

I NOTE, WITH SOME DISMAY, YOU'VE CHOSEN TO JUMP THE LEDGE.

RIGHT. AND **THAT** DECISION WILL GIVE US **NEW** CHOICES.

LIKE, SHOULD WE BAIL OUT OR DIE IN THE LANDING?

EXACTLY. OUR FIRST DECISION CREATED A CHAIN REACTION OF DECISIONS. LET'S JUMP.

SEE? IF YOU DON'T MAKE EACH DECISION CAREFULLY, YOU NEVER KNOW **WHERE** YOU'LL END UP. THAT'S AN IMPORTANT LESSON WE SHOULD LEARN SOMETIME.

I WISH WE COULD TALK ABOUT THESE THINGS WITHOUT THE VISUAL AIDS.

TODAY FOR "SHOW AND TELL", I HAVE A SOUVENIR FROM THE AFTERLIFE! YES, YOU HEARD RIGHT! EQUALLY AMAZING IS MY OWN STORY OF YESTERDAY AFTERNOON, WHEN I ACTUALLY DIED OF BOREDOM!

I WAS DOING MY HOMEWORK, WHEN SUDDENLY I COLLAPSED! I FELT MYSELF RISING, AND I COULD SEE MY CRUMPLED BODY ON THE FLOOR. I DRIFTED UP IN A SHAFT OF LIGHT AND I ENTERED THE NEXT WORLD!

EVENTUALLY, MY HEART STARTED AGAIN AND I CAME BACK TO LIFE ... BUT NOT BEFORE BRINGING THIS BACK!

A YO-YO?

IT WAS PRETTY BORING THERE, TOO.

LET'S HAVE A LOOK AT THAT HOMEWORK.

AND SO, HAVING EATEN HER FILL, THE MOTHER BIRD RETURNS TO HER NEST...

..WHERE SHE REGURGITATES THE WORMS TO FEED HER HUNGRY BROOD.

..SIGHHHHHH...

CALVIN, PAY ATTENTION!

NUGH

THERE'S NO HEAD REST ON THIS CHAIR! I SHOULD SUE FOR WHIPLASH!

CALVIN and HOBBES
by WATTERSON

ARE YOU GOING TO READ CALVIN A STORY?

ONLY IF IT'S NOT THAT AWFUL "HAMSTER HUEY AND THE GOOEY KABLOOIE".

OH, BUT YOU LOOK SO *CUTE* DOING THE "HAPPY HAMSTER HOP"!

I DON'T *WANT* TO LOOK CUTE!!

WHAT STORY WOULD YOU LIKE TONIGHT, CALVIN?

I WANT A STORY ABOUT HOBBES AND ME.

OK... HMM... LET'S SEE... ONCE THERE WAS A BOY NAMED CALVIN WHO LIVED WITH A TIGER NAMED HOBBES.

THIS IS GREAT!

TODAY THEY GOT UP AT THE CRACK OF DAWN AND MADE A HUGE RUCKUS RUNNING *UP* THE STAIRS, GALUMP, GALUMP, GALUMP, AND SLIDING *DOWN* AGAIN, BUMP, BUMP BUMP, BUMP!

YEAH, THEN THE *BIG BAD DAD* YELLED THAT IF WE DIDN'T KNOCK IT OFF, HE'D MAIL US TO *PLUTO* THIRD CLASS!

WHO'S TELLING THIS STORY, YOU OR ME?

YOU *DID* SAY THAT! DON'T TRY TO DENY IT!

SO FINALLY, CALVIN GOT THE HINT AND HE WENT TO ROT HIS INNARDS WITH CHOCOLATE CEREAL, AND TO ROT HIS BRAIN WATCHING CARTOONS.

HEY! *NO* EDITORIALS!

AT LAST CALVIN AND HOBBES WENT OUTSIDE, AND IT WAS NICE AND QUIET IN THE HOUSE AGAIN. AT LEAST FOR A WHILE. WELL, GOOD NIGHT.'

GOOD NIGHT? THAT'S NOT THE END! YOU DIDN'T EVEN GET US TO LUNCHTIME!

THAT'S RIGHT... IT'S NOT THE END OF THE STORY. THIS STORY DOESN'T *HAVE* AN END. YOU AND HOBBES WILL WRITE *MORE* OF IT TOMORROW AND EVERY DAY AFTER. BUT NOW IT'S TIME TO SLEEP, SO GOOD NIGHT.

OH! OK, GOOD NIGHT.

THIS *IS* A GOOD STORY ABOUT US IF IT DOESN'T END! THAT'S THE KIND OF STORY I LIKE BEST! GOOD NIGHT, OL' BUDDY!

ME TOO! SEE YOU TOMORROW!

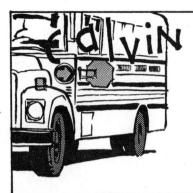

CALVIN and HOBBES by WATTERSON

I'M FREEEEEEEEEEEEEEEEEE

HO HO! THEY *TRIED* TO MAKE ME LEARN, BUT *I* WAS TOO *TOUGH* FOR 'EM!

I'M HOME!

WHY HELLO, CALVIN! DO COME IN, WON'T YOU?

CLICK.

HEY! HEY!

MAY I READ ALL YOUR COMIC BOOKS? I *MAY*? THANK YOU, CALVIN!

MAY I DRAW MUSTACHES ON ALL THE SUPERHEROES? I *MAY*? OH JOY!

I'LL GET HIM FOR THIS IF IT TAKES MY WHOLE LIFE.

I'VE COME UP WITH A NEW SYSTEM FOR DOING HOMEWORK. I CALL IT "EFFECTIVE TIME MANAGEMENT," OR "ETM" FOR SHORT.

I'VE DRAWN UP A SCHEDULE FOR EACH SCHOOL SUBJECT, AND I USE THIS KITCHEN TIMER TO MONITOR MY PACE.

THANKS TO ETM, I'M MUCH MORE EFFICIENT, AND MY WORK GOES FASTER!

RINGG

THERE! MY MATH MINUTE IS UP! SET THE CLOCK FOR MY SPELLING ASSIGNMENT, OK?

UM, YOUR SCHEDULE CALLS FOR SMALLER TIME INCREMENTS THAN THIS CLOCK CAN MEASURE.

NO I WON'T TAKE A PICTURE OF YOU.

KA

ZAM!

WHAT?

CALVIN and HOBBES

by WATTERSON

TOAD STROGANOFF!

..EWWWW..

POKE POKE

AUGH!

CLINK
CLINK
CLINK

HA!

SPLORPP!

SPLAT!

DON'T BLAME ME. I'M THE ONE WHO SAID WE SHOULD CALL FOR A PIZZA.

EWW! WHAT **IS** THIS?! IT LOOKS LIKE **COMPOST**!

MOM DOESN'T APPRECIATE ME.

HEY HOBBES, WHAT'S A "PAPER TIGER"?

IT'S LIKE A PAPER BOY. YOU KNOW, A TIGER WITH A NEWSPAPER ROUTE.

OH.

THIS BOOK MAKES NO SENSE AT ALL.

HEY DAD, WOULD YOU PAY ME A DOLLAR TO EAT A BUG?

NO, YOU'D HAVE TO EAT A BUCKET OF BUGS BEFORE I'D PAY YOU A DOLLAR.

A WHOLE BUCKET?

OR I'D PAY YOU A DOLLAR TO PICK UP STICKS IN THE BACK YARD.

ALL MY **REAL** SKILLS ARE UNDERVALUED.

ON DISTANT PLANET ZARK, WE FIND THE EMPTY RED SPACECRAFT OF OUR HERO, THE BOLD *SPACEMAN SPIFF!*

UH OH! UP AHEAD, THE ROCKS ARE CHARRED WITH DEATH RAY BLASTS! A VIOLENT STRUGGLE TOOK PLACE HERE!

AND ONLY THE TRACKS OF A LARGE, SINISTER ALIEN LEAVE THE SCENE! WHAT HAS HAPPENED TO THE EARTHLING EXPLORER?

CALVIN, THIS IS HUMILIATING!!

I DON'T WANT TO GO! PUT ME DOWN!

SPACEMAN SPIFF IS BEING HELD PRISONER BY HIDEOUS ALIENS! WHAT DO THEY WANT WITH HIM?

SPIFF IS SOON TO FIND OUT! OUR HERO IS CALLED BEFORE THE ALIEN POTENTATE!

..WHERE IT BECOMES CLEAR THAT SPIFF IS ABOUT TO BE *SACRIFICED...*

..TO APPEASE THE EVIL GOD THEY CALL "NOLLIJ"!

UP TO THE BLACKBOARD. HURRY UP.

STARING DEATH IN THE FACE, OUR HERO THINKS FAST.

$11 - 4 =$

INCHING CLOSER TO THE SACRIFICIAL PIT, SPIFF SLOWLY AND SMOOTHLY REACHES FOR THE TINY ATOM BLASTER CONCEALED IN HIS BELT!

YAA! ALL RIGHT, YOU BLOODSUCKING, MUTANT CHROMOSOMAL DISASTERS! NOBODY MOVE! I'M OUTTA HERE!

CALVIN, GIVE ME THAT RUBBER BAND RIGHT THIS MINUTE!

I SAID NOBODY MOVE!

SPIFF ESCAPES! THE DANK AND SMELLY CORRIDORS OF THE ALIEN FORTRESS ARE DESERTED! ALL THE ALIENS HAD GATHERED FOR THE SPECTACLE OF OUR HERO'S DEMISE!

THE FEARLESS SPACE EXPLORER MAKES IT TO THE PLANET SURFACE, BUT THE ALIEN QUEEN IS IN PURSUIT!

CALVIN, GET BACK HERE!

SPIFF JUMPS INTO THE COCKPIT, PRESSURIZES THE LAUNCH THRUSTERS, AND...

BLASTS OFF! OUR HERO IS SAFE!

Tomorrow: OR *IS* HE ??

CALVIN! WHAT ARE YOU DOING HOME?! IT'S NOT EVEN NOON!

UH, THEY LET US OUT EARLY TODAY. THERE WAS, UM, A GAS LEAK.

WHAT?! DOES ANYONE KNOW YOU LEFT?! I'M CALLING THE SCHOOL.

DON'T WASTE YOUR TIME! EVERYONE WAS EVACUATED! THERE'S NOBODY THERE!

HELLO? ELEMENTARY SCHOOL OFFICE, PLEASE.

OUR HERO HADN'T COUNTED ON RUNNING INTO A ZARK ENFORCER SHIP! SPIFF'S EVASIVE MANEUVERS COME TO NAUGHT! THIS COULD BE THE END!

BOY, I SURE GOT IN BIG TROUBLE *TODAY!* MOM HIT THE ROOF WHEN SHE FOUND OUT I JUST LEFT SCHOOL.

WHAT HAPPENED?

SHE DROVE ME BACK AND WE HAD TO TALK TO MY TEACHER *AND* THE PRINCIPAL! THEY TALKED ABOUT MY STUDY HABITS, AND NOW I'VE GOT EXTRA HOMEWORK!

OOH.

AND DAD IS GOING TO CHECK IT EVERY NIGHT TO MAKE SURE IT'S DONE RIGHT! CAN YOU BELIEVE IT?!

SO TRY TO DO AN EXTRA GOOD JOB NOW, OK?

YOU'RE LUCKY TIGERS ARE SO SMART.

Calvin and Hobbes by Watterson

ANOTHER PLANET, ANOTHER SWEEPING PANORAMA OF INDESCRIBABLE GRANDEUR!

THE INCREDIBLE SPACEMAN SPIFF ZOOMS TO THE SURFACE OF AHNOOIE-4!

TOUCHING DOWN, OUR HERO SETS OFF TO SEARCH FOR SENTIENT LIFE!

ALAS, SPACEMAN SPIFF ONLY DISCOVERS A HIDEOUS BLOB SO MONUMENTALLY STUPID THAT IT JUST STARES STRAIGHT AHEAD, COMPLETELY UNAWARE OF ANYTHING AROUND IT!

COMPASSIONATELY, OUR HERO DECIDES TO PUT THE BLOB OUT OF ITS MISERY. SPIFF SETS HIS BLASTER ON "LIQUEFY."

EWW! MISS WORMWOOD! CALVIN'S SHOOTING SPIT BALLS!

PERPLEXED BY THE BLOB'S RESILIENCE, SPIFF ADDS MORE JUICE AND PREPARES TO FIRE AGAIN!

114

UFOs! ARE THEY REAL?? HAVE THEY LANDED IN OUR TOWNS AND NEIGHBORHOODS?

DO THE CHILLING PHOTOGRAPHS BY AN AMATEUR PHOTOGRAPHER REALLY SHOW A SINISTER ALIEN SPACESHIP AND THE GRIM RESULTS OF A CLOSE ENCOUNTER, OR ARE THE PICTURES AN ELABORATE HOAX?

LISTEN TO AN EXPERT ON SPACE ALIENS SPECULATE ON THEIR HIDEOUS BIOLOGY AND THEIR HORRIFYING WEAPONRY! ALL THIS AND MORE...

...ON CALVIN'S SHOW AND TELL ... *NEXT!*

CALVIN, WILL YOU COME HERE PLEASE?

TWITCHING TUFTED TAIL, A TOASTY, TAWNY TUMMY: A TIRED TIGER.

...AN ALLITERATIVE HAIKU BY CALVIN. THANK YOU, THANK YOU.

SHEESH.

YOU KNOW HOW PEOPLE LOOK AT MODERN ART AND ALWAYS SAY, "MY 6-YEAR-OLD KID COULD DO THAT!"?

WELL, THAT GAVE ME THIS GREAT IDEA! I'VE DECIDED TO BECOME A FORGER AND GET RICH PASSING OFF FAKE PAINTINGS TO MUSEUMS!

A LOT OF PAINTINGS SELL FOR TENS OF MILLIONS OF DOLLARS NOW, SO I MAKE A PRETTY GOOD HOURLY RATE.

YOU SHOULD PROBABLY SCRATCH OUT THE COPYRIGHT DATE ON THE CARTOON STATIONERY.

OOH YEAH, GLAD YOU CAUGHT THAT!

Calvin and Hobbes

by WATTERSON

HISTORICAL MARKER "CALVIN'S HOUSE" IN JANUARY, SOME 40 SNOWMEN MET A GRUESOME FATE ON THIS SPOT.

EVERY DAY I LOOK FOR A MOVING VAN HERE.

KNOCK KNOCK

GREAT MOONS OF NEPTUNE! A FOOL MORTAL FEMALE!

CALVIN?

I'M NOT CALVIN! I'M STUPENDOUS MAN! FRIEND OF FREEDOM! OPPONENT OF OPPRESSION!

UH HUH. WHAT ARE YOU DOING?

I WAS JUST ABOUT TO USE MY STUPENDOUS POWERS TO LIBERATE SOME COOKIES BEING HELD HOSTAGE ON THE TOP SHELF OF THE PANTRY! NOW IF YOU'LL EXCUSE ME, DUTY CALLS!

SLAM!

A BOLT OF CRIMSON STREAKS ACROSS THE SKY! THE MAN OF MEGA-MIGHT IS OFF TO SAVE THE DAY!

DID THEY HAVE AN EGG YOU COULD BORROW?

NO ONE WAS HOME, MOM.

Calvin and Hobbes
by WATTERSON

MY LIFE COULD BE A LOT BETTER THAN IT IS.

I'M HAPPY, BUT IT'S NOT LIKE I'M ECSTATIC.

LIFE IS LIKE TOPOGRAPHY, HOBBES. THERE ARE SUMMITS OF HAPPINESS AND SUCCESS...

...FLAT STRETCHES OF BORING ROUTINE...

...AND VALLEYS OF FRUSTRATION AND FAILURE.

BUT I'M DEDICATING MYSELF TO EXPERIENCING ONLY PEAKS! I WANT MY LIFE TO BE ONE NEVER ENDING ASCENSION!

EACH MINUTE OF EVERY DAY SHOULD BRING ME GREATER JOY THAN THE PREVIOUS MINUTE!

I SHOULD ALWAYS BE SAYING, "MY LIFE IS BETTER THAN I EVER IMAGINED IT WOULD BE, AND IT'S ONLY GOING TO IMPROVE."

I'M JUST GOING TO JUMP FROM PEAK TO PEAK! I'M... WHOOPS.

AT LEAST WITH FLAT PLACES, YOU DON'T HAVE SO FAR TO GO DOWN.

ONLY LOSERS GO DOWN! FOR ME IT'S ONLY GOING TO BE UP AND UP!

CLICK.

PANDER TO ME!

PLAYING A RECORD? I'LL SHOW YOU SOMETHING INTERESTING.

COMPARE A POINT ON THE LABEL WITH A POINT ON THE RECORD'S OUTER EDGE. THEY BOTH MAKE A COMPLETE CIRCLE IN THE SAME AMOUNT OF TIME, RIGHT?

YEAH...

BUT THE POINT ON THE RECORD'S EDGE HAS TO MAKE A BIGGER CIRCLE IN THE SAME TIME, SO IT GOES FASTER. SEE, TWO POINTS ON ONE DISK MOVE AT TWO SPEEDS, EVEN THOUGH THEY BOTH MAKE THE SAME REVOLUTIONS PER MINUTE!

ON YOUR MARK... GET SET... GO!

I'M GOING SO SLOW, I'M MOVING BACKWARD! I'M WINNING!

THAT'S CHEATING!

119

CaLViN aNd HObbEs

by WATTERSON

UH-O

OH NO! EVERYTHING HAS SUDDENLY TURNED NEO-CUBIST!

IT ALL STARTED WHEN CALVIN ENGAGED HIS DAD IN A MINOR DEBATE! SOON CALVIN COULD SEE BOTH SIDES OF THE ISSUE! THEN POOR CALVIN BEGAN TO SEE BOTH SIDES OF *EVERY*THING!

THE TRADITIONAL SINGLE VIEWPOINT HAS BEEN ABANDONED! PERSPECTIVE HAS BEEN FRACTURED!

THE MULTIPLE VIEWS PROVIDE TOO MUCH INFORMATION! IT'S IMPOSSIBLE TO MOVE! CALVIN QUICKLY TRIES TO ELIMINATE ALL BUT ONE PERSPECTIVE!

IT WORKS! THE WORLD FALLS INTO A RECOGNIZABLE ORDER!

YOU'RE STILL WRONG, DAD.

CalViN aND HobbEs
by WATTERSON

OH CALVIN, WOULD YOU PLEASE EMPTY THIS IN THE GARAGE TRASH CAN?

BOY, SOME VACATION *THIS* SUMMER IS!

WHAT'S *THIS* UGLY BRUTE CALLED?

AN ALLO-SAUR!

I'M RIGHT HERE. YOU DON'T NEED TO SHOUT.

RUN!

WHEN WE GET TO THE TIME MACHINE THROW HIM THE SNACKS WE PACKED! MAYBE THAT WILL DIVERT HIM WHILE WE TAKE OFF!

YOU CAN THROW *YOUR* SNACKS. I MIGHT STILL WANT MINE.

YOU'RE GOING TO BE A SNACK YOURSELF! GET IN! GET IN!

QUICK! THROW HIM THE FOOD!

MY SANDWICH HAD MUSTARD. IS THIS ONE YOURS?

PUT ON YOUR VORTEX GOGGLES! WE'RE TAKING OFF!

EWW, THIS BANANA IS MUSHY. HE CAN HAVE *THIS*.

WE DID IT! WE'RE OFF!

HERE.

BOY, THAT WAS A CLOSE CALL, BUT IT WILL BE WORTH IT WHEN WE GET THESE PICTURES DEVELOPED.

SINCE I RESCUED YOUR SANDWICH, CAN I EAT IT?

HEY MOM, GUESS WHERE HOBBES AND I HAVE BEEN!

I *SAW* WHERE YOU WERE. YOU WERE PLAYING IN A CARDBOARD BOX OUT BACK.

NOPE! THAT'S JUST WHAT IT *LOOKED* LIKE.

WE TIME-TRAVELED TO THE JURASSIC, BUT WE RETURNED AT THE SPLIT SECOND WE LEFT! THAT'S WHY IT DIDN'T LOOK LIKE WE WERE GONE! WE SAW LOTS OF DINOSAURS!

WELL, YOU'VE HAD A PRODUCTIVE MORNING THEN.

YEAH. WILL YOU TAKE THIS FILM TO BE DEVELOPED? I'LL PAY YOU BACK WHEN TIME MAGAZINE COUGHS UP FOR MY STORY.

Panel 1: HOBBES, LOOK! WE GOT OUR PICTURES BACK FROM OUR JURASSIC TRIP! / OH BOY! LET'S SEE!

Panel 2: WOW, THESE CAME OUT GOOD! LOOK AT THAT APATOSAUR! / THERE'S ME! THERE'S ME!

Panel 3: YES! YES! WE'RE RICH! HA HA! NOW WE CAN GET OUR OWN APARTMENT! / THIS DINOSAUR BLINKED.

Panel 4: I'LL BUY A CAR TOO, BUT SINCE I CAN'T DRIVE FOR ANOTHER DECADE, WE'LL HAVE TO GET A CHAUFFEUR. / IF WE PAY HIM, HE HAS TO LET US SIT UP FRONT AND BEEP THE HORN, RIGHT?

Panel 5: WELL DAD, IT'S TOO BAD YOU WEREN'T ANY NICER TO ME ALL THESE YEARS.

Panel 6: BEG PARDON? / YEP, I CAN'T SAY I'M PARTICULARLY INCLINED TO SHARE MY FUTURE MILLIONS WITH YOU. HERE, LOOK.

Panel 7: DINOSAURS? / HOBBES AND I WENT TO THE JURASSIC TODAY AND CAME BACK WITH THESE DRAMATIC PHOTOGRAPHS! WE'RE GOING TO BE RICH!

Panel 8: I DIDN'T REALIZE DINOSAURS LOOKED SO SMALL AND PLASTIC. / HEY, WHAT ARE YOU INSINUATING?!

Panel 9: DAD DOESN'T BELIEVE WE WENT TO THE JURASSIC AND TOOK PHOTOGRAPHS OF REAL DINOSAURS.

Panel 10: HE SAYS IT LOOKS LIKE WE JUST PUT MY TOY MODELS IN THE YARD AND TOOK PICTURES OF THEM! HE SAYS OUR GET-RICH-QUICK SCHEME WON'T WORK.

Panel 11: HUH! / HE SAID IF WE REALLY WANTED TO GET SOME MONEY, HE'D PAY US A DOLLAR TO PULL WEEDS OUT OF THE FRONT WALK.

Panel 12: JUST A DOLLAR? / OF COURSE I TOLD HIM WE DIDN'T WANT THE MONEY THAT BAD.

Calvin and Hobbes

by WATTERSON

ANOTHER ONE OF *THESE* DAYS.

UH OH! IN ANOTHER OF LIFE'S MYSTERIOUS QUIRKS, CALVIN FINDS HIMSELF AN INCH TALL ON THE WRITING DESK!

HIS ONLY HOPE IS TO TEAR OFF A SHEET FROM A NEARBY PAD OF PAPER!

AT HIS TINY SIZE, FOLDING THE SHEET IS DIFFICULT, BUT SOON CALVIN'S PATIENCE IS REWARDED!

HE PUSHES OFF AND CATCHES A SMALL THERMAL RISING UP THE FRONT OF THE DESK!

A GUST FROM AN OPEN WINDOW SENDS CALVIN SOARING ACROSS THE HOUSE!

THERE'S DAD! LEAN! LEAN!

YES! CALVIN IS ABLE TO STEER! *THIS* SHOULD GET DAD'S ATTENTION!

I DON'T NEED PARENTS. ALL I NEED IS A RECORDING THAT SAYS, "GO PLAY OUTSIDE!"

The End